American Stoneflies:

A Photographic Guide to the Plecoptera

Bill P. Stark
Stanley W. Szczytko
C. Riley Nelson

The Caddis Press, Columbus, Ohio   1998

Title Page Illustration

Calliperla luctuosa, male and female — OR: Curry Co. Seeps in Elk River Canyon. 2.vi.1991. B. Stark, R. Baumann, and C. Henderson. Photograph by Bill Stark.

Distributor

For all countries: The Caddis Press, P.O. Box 21039, Columbus, Ohio 43221-0039 U.S.A.

Cataloging

ISBN 0-9667982-0-1
Library of Congress 98-88319

Copyright

Literature Citation

Stark, Bill P., Stanley W. Szczytko, and C. Riley Nelson. 1998. American Stoneflies: A Photographic Guide to the Plecoptera, The Caddis Press. Columbus, Ohio. iv + 126 p.

Credits

Technical Editor:	Brian J. Armitage, The Caddis Press
Layout and Design:	Brian J. Armitage, The Caddis Press
Printing:	The Ohio State University Printing Services, Columbus, Ohio U.S.A.

11-1998—5.0M

Acknowledgments

This project would not have been possible without the support of our colleagues and students. We especially thank Boris Kondratieff, Rich Bottoroff, Gene Fiala, Fred Kirchner, and Barry Poulton for their generous contributions of live specimens. We also thank the Mississippi College and University of Wisconsin-Stevens Point students and our colleague Dick Baumann, who accompanied us on collecting trips from 1989-1995 as we accumulated photographs. Finally we acknowledge Brian Armitage and The Caddis Press for their essential role in bringing this project to fruition.

Table of Contents

CHAPTER 1

INTRODUCTION

In the early spring of 1963, one of us [BPS] was enrolled in an undergraduate entomology class when the instructor led an expedition to a nearby stream to collect stoneflies. Armed with a statement from the H. H. Ross textbook that they "...show a decided preference for concrete bridges and may be collected in great numbers there," we went forth already counting the points we would gain with the addition of Capniidae, Leuctridae and Taeniopterygidae to our hoard of specimens. Unfortunately, no stoneflies were taken by this group of novices, but I was smitten, permanently, it seems, by the stonefly bug that day. Each of the authors has been infected in this fashion, and we have frequently gone "in search of" the elusive stonefly. Over the past few years as we accumulated photographs for this project, our work led us through the Rockies from New Mexico to Alberta, through the Coast and Cascade Ranges from southern California to British Columbia and into the Ozarks, Ouachitas, and Appalachians. Additional photographs were made of local species, or of specimens mailed to us by colleagues, on our respective home turfs in Mississippi, Wisconsin or Texas. What is it about these obscure insects that so fascinates a person to devote their lifetime to the pursuit and study of the stonefly? In this small volume we hope to provide some insight into the beauty and diversity of this group in North America, and perhaps in the presentation, provide an answer to this question.

WHAT ARE STONEFLIES?

Stoneflies are a small order of insects whose immature stage, the nymph, is aquatic. The approximately 600 North American species are placed in some 100 genera and nine families (Table 1.1). The ordinal name, Plecoptera (literally, "folded wings"), refers to the anal lobe of the hind wing which is typically folded under the anterior portion of the wing when the insect is at rest. In addition to this feature, stoneflies are usually recognized by the two tails, or cerci, and by the presence of three tarsal segments on each leg.

Plecoptera as a group has little direct impact on human society and a probable low recognition value among the general public. However, cases of plecopterophobia may have occurred when emerging *Allocapnia* were discovered entering a Connecticut school (Hitchcock, 1974), or when *Paraperla* nymphs were found in the Eureka, Montana, domestic water supply (Stanford and Gaufin, 1974). Outside the entomological community, and the people affected by such isolated cases, stoneflies are perhaps best known to trout anglers. The recent Robert Redford film, "A River Runs Through It," includes a scene based on this knowledge when one of the characters in the movie uses a fly modeled after a stonefly which had landed on him. Stoneflies have also long been recognized as indicators of clean water conditions. Because of their sensitivity to an array of stream disturbances such as sedimentation, pesticides, and organic pollution, stonefly populations in many areas are now threatened by human activity.

Despite these problems and their general lack of recognition, stoneflies have great ecological value in stream ecosystems. Many species, including the giant salmonflies, are important shredders of leaves which fall into streams. These shredder species convert an organic resource of large particle size into smaller particles through feeding and defecation. These smaller organic particles are carried in stream currents and captured by many other organisms which feed as collectors and filterers. This role may be likened to that of the elephants whose fecal material, still rich in plant fiber, is colonized by beetles and other dung feeders in terrestrial ecosystems of Africa. Other stoneflies are regarded as top carnivores, particularly in spring or seepage habitats, where they may compete with salamander larvae, and all stoneflies, regardless of niche, contribute to the food base of various local insect eating vertebrates such as dippers, nighthawks, bats, and fish.

STONEFLY ANATOMY

Stoneflies, like other insects, display three distinct body regions (Figs. 1.1-1.2). The head region bears a pair of long and multisegmented antennae, mouthparts, a pair of compound eyes, and two or three ocelli. The mouthparts include a simple upper lip or labrum, a pair of hardened and multi-toothed mandibles, a pair of maxillae which terminate in hardened laciniae bearing 1-3 teeth, and a multilobed lower lip or labium. Mandibular, maxillary and labial structures generally reflect nymphal feeding preferences. The primarily carnivorous species have one or two slender lacinial teeth, long paraglossae, and long labial palps. While the species which feed primarily on plant materials have three thickened lacinial teeth, short paraglossae, and short labial palps. Many adult stoneflies lack the hardened mandibles and maxillae of their nymphal counterparts and consequently, may not feed. Small, fleshy outgrowths known as submental gills are found at the labial base in some members of Perlodidae, and branched or single gills occur in the neck region of some Peltoperlidae, Perlodidae, and Nemouridae.

The thorax includes three segments, the pro-, meso- and metathorax. Each thoracic segment bears a pair of legs, and the meso- and metathoracic segments each have a pair of wings in the adult, or wing pads in the nymphs. Legs consist of a basal coxa, a short trochanter, a prominent femur, a long slender tibia, three tarsal segments, and a pair of apical tarsal claws. The relative lengths of the two basal tarsal segments is an important characteristic distinguishing stonefly families. Wings are typically folded over the abdominal segments but in some species these may be shortened (brachypterous or micropterous) or absent (apterous). Several variations in wing venation are useful in recognizing stonefly adults at the family level, particularly those in the anal region. Major longitudinal veins from front margin to rear margin are: Costa (C), Subcosta (Sc), Radius (R), Media (M), Cubitus (Cu), and Anal (A). Pteronarcyid stoneflies have numerous crossveins scattered through the wings but species in most other groups exhibit few crossveins other than in the costal and cubito-median regions.

Many immature stoneflies have gills on the thoracic segments, particularly around the leg bases, and in some instances, these may be retained as vestigial structures in the adult. Thoracic gills may be simple, finger-like, and fleshy-appearing, or complexly lobed structures consisting of numerous slender filaments; some species exhibit forked or bilobed gills.

The abdominal region is 10-segmented and bears a pair of apical cerci. All nymphal stoneflies have multisegmented cerci which frequently are about as long as the abdomen; some adult stoneflies have these shortened to a few, or as in the Leuctridae, Nemouridae, and some Taeniopterygidae, to a single segment. Adults also have various types of probes, hooks, lobes, and slots comprising the genitalia on the terminal abdominal segments (Figs. 1.3-1.8). The female genitalia are relatively simple and usually consist of an opening on the ventral side of the eighth abdominal segment, often covered by a flap-like subgenital plate (Fig. 1.8). Male genitalia consist of structures on the dorsum and apex of the abdomen, or retracted within a cavity on the ninth or tenth abdominal segment (Figs. 1.3-1.5). These structures

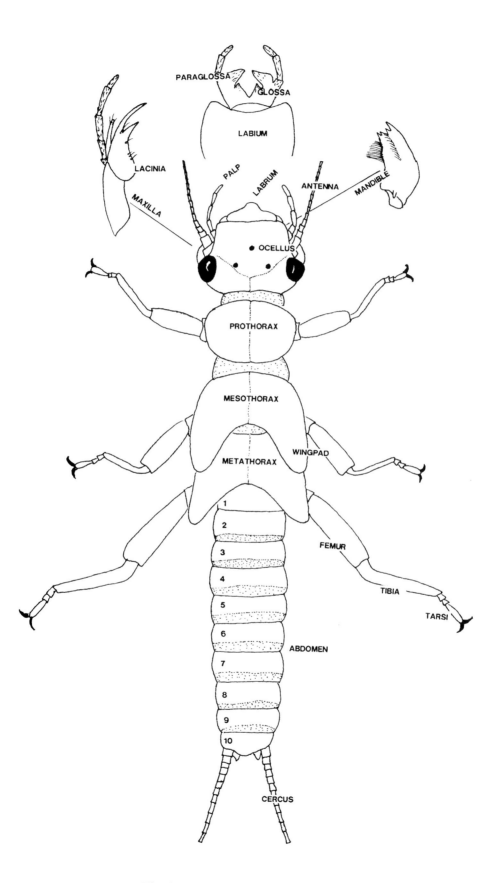

Fig. 1.1. Generalized stonefly nymph.

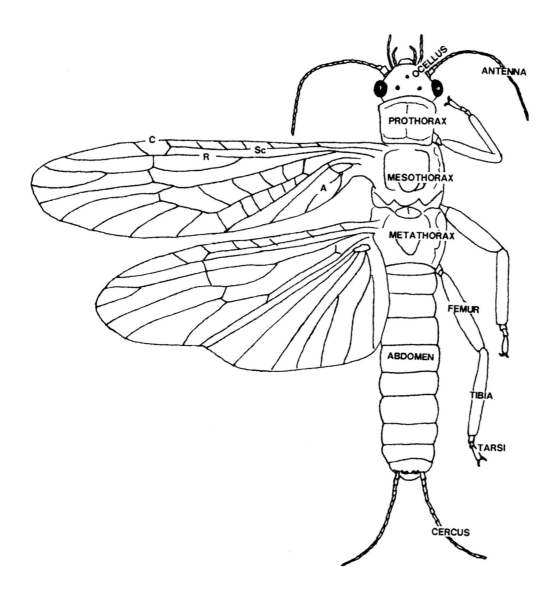

Fig. 1.2. Generalized stonefly adult.

provide the male with sensory information assisting in mating, and they are involved in delivery of sperm. Males of several groups exhibit dorsal probes known as epiprocts, apical hooks known as paraprocts or dorsal lobes on abdominal segments 5-10. Many males also have modifications for sound production on one or more terminal ventral segments. These percussion instruments usually take the form of a thickened, callus-like hammer, or a flap-like vesicle. Males tap out signals with these devices as they attempt to locate mates; females usually respond by tapping a return signal, however, they lack special structures for sound production.

Gills of the same form as those found on the thorax may occur on abdominal segments of Pteronarcyidae, certain Perlodidae, or in the anal area of some Perlidae.

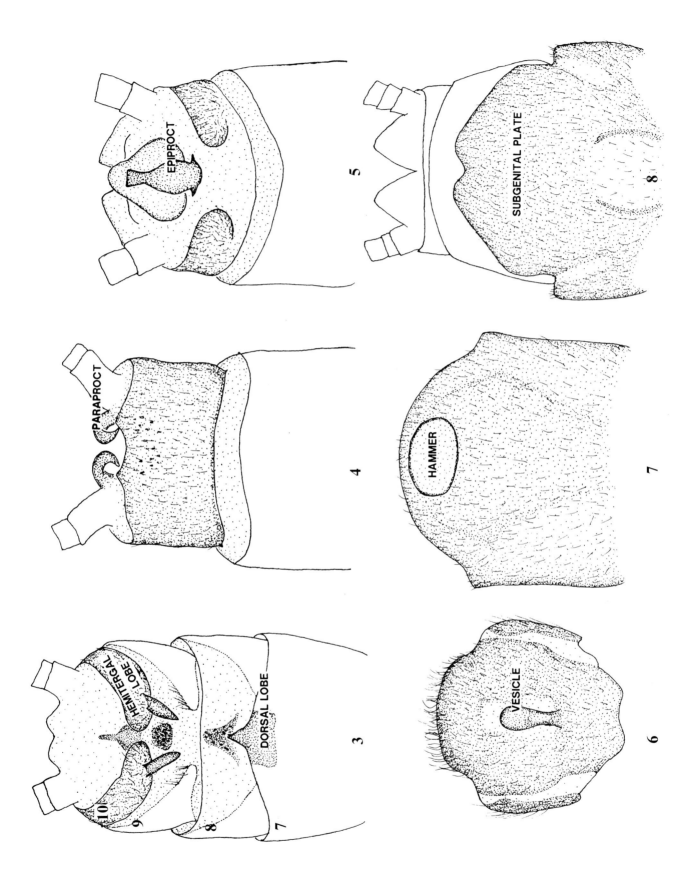

Figs. 1.3-1.8. Stonefly external genitalic structures. 1.3-1.5, Variations in male structures. 1.6-1.7, Male 9th sterna showing drumming structures. 1.8, Typical female structure.

Eggs of stoneflies display considerable variation in size, shape and details of chorionic (egg shell) ornamentation (Fig. 1.9). Many species have spindle shaped eggs, but spherical, flattened, and 3-sided examples are known; frequently an anterior collar is present. The chorionic surface may be smooth but typically some hexagonal pattern of impressions formed by cells lining the ovarian chambers where eggs are produced is evident. Specialized sperm entrance holes, the micropyles, penetrate the chorion completely, while shallower pores may lead to elaborate respiratory networks within the chorion. When eggs are deposited in the water, sticky membranous or gelatinous materials outside the chorion swell and attach the egg to a substrate.

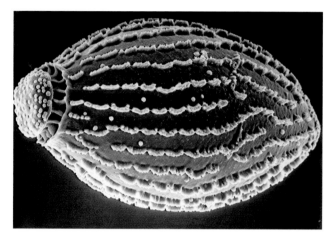

Fig. 1.9. Egg structure of *Kathroperla perdita*.

Embryonic development may proceed directly, with hatching occuring within a few weeks, or the egg may enter diapause, a period of dormancy or arrested development, and hatch much later. In some diapausing species, this adaptation, presumably, enables the insect to survive during adverse conditions such as periods of extreme heat, cold, or dryness.

After hatching, the first instar nymphs are soft bodied, unpigmented, and have short, 3-5 segmented cerci. Nymphal diapause has been reported in some species but in most cases, feeding and growth begin immediately after hatching and continues for 1-3 years until the nymph is in a pre-emergent condition. Two general growth patterns are recognized for American stoneflies. "Fast cycle" species undergo either nymphal or egg diapause usually for several months, then grow quickly over a 3-4 month period and emerge as adults. "Slow cycle" species hatch directly and grow, more or less, continuously over a 1-3 year period until emergence. During the nymphal growth period, the stonefly periodically molts (Fig. 1.10). Following this event, the insect is again soft bodied and unpigmented for a brief period, and legs or other appendages lost during the previous stage may appear as abnormally small, regenerated structures. Emergence occurs when mature nymphs (Fig. 1.11) crawl out of the water on rocks, sticks, plants, or other objects, but emergence under ice cover is common for some capniids and other winter-emerging species. The nymphal skin is split along suture lines of the head and thoracic segments and the adult struggles from its covering with crumpled wings and a soft, unpigmented body (Fig. 1.12). Within an hour or so the wings harden, pigments develop, and adults scatter from emergence sites to begin the next phase characterized by mating activity.

Many adult stoneflies engage in a pre-mating ritual which includes the exchange of signals produced by tapping the abdominal apex on twigs, leaves or other substrata. This "drumming" activity typically involves a species specific male call, a female answer and sometimes a male response (Stewart et al., 1983). Males receiving answers from receptive females engage in searching behavior, sometimes using repeated calls, until the female is located. Mating occurs when the male mounts the female, curves his abdomen around her body and engages the subgenital plate with his genitalia (Fig. 1.18). Sperm are usually introduced inside the female genital capsule, but in some species an externally deposited sperm mass is drawn into the genital capsule by the female. Females typically mate only once, and after the eggs have matured the females produce small pellets containing several hundred eggs which they hold on the subgenital plates of their upturned abdomens. Females undergo oviposition flights, splashing the water surface as they release their mass of eggs. Survivors may repeat this oviposition process several times as additional egg masses are produced over a period of several days to a few weeks.

[Clockwise from upper left]

Fig. 1.10. Hatching Isoperla lata nymph. WI, Lincoln Co., Ripley Creek, 21.vi.1992, S. Szczytko.

Fig. 1.11. Pre-emergent nymph of *Beloneuria georgiana*. Darkened wingpads indicate this specimen is ready to emerge. GA: Murray Co., 29.v.1993, B. Stark, R. Simmons, D. Kelly.

Fig. 1.12. Recently emerged adult of *Paragnetina media*. WI: Menominee Co., Wolf River, 6.vi.1991, S. Szczytko, J. Dimick, J. Sandberg.

COLLECTING STONEFLIES

Stonefly nymphs are usually found in riffle areas of streams (Fig. 1.13) where they hide under rocks, in gravel, and in accumulated leaf packs or other debris. A few species occur in lakes, particularly those at high altitudes or northern latitudes, and some species inhabit spring seepage areas and splash zones created by spray from water falls. In riffles, they can be collected by disturbing the rocks and debris immediately above a net or screen (Fig. 1.16), but in seepage areas they are most easily taken by carefully sorting through leaves, sticks and rocks by hand (Fig. 1.14). In general, streams of different sizes may support different species assemblages and in mountainous areas, species generally vary along altitudinal gradients. Adults of many species are attracted to lights near streams on warm nights, but good numbers of specimens may be collected using the "beating sheet" method, or by sweeping streamside vegetation with a net. Some species also hide under rocks or in crevices of logs where they may be discovered by carefully searching these areas (Fig. 1.15). Occasionally, large numbers of specimens may be collected with a standard insect net as the females return to the stream to oviposit. Collecting stoneflies in this fashion can be challenging as well as rewarding, since they are only briefly visible as they rise from the water in the dusk. While engaged in this sport, we may have inadvertently entertained a few passersby near Tomahawk, Wisconsin, in August 1992, but so far our actions have not surfaced on any "Amazing Home Video" shows.

Fig. 1.14. Ken Stewart, University of North Texas stonefly specialist, searches rocks and debris in Logan Creek, Montana, for nymphs of a rare nemourid, *Lednia tumana.*

Fig. 1.13. Logan Pass, Glacier National Park, Montana, is a familar location for tourists, but Logan Creek, which cascades into a small meadow in the pass, is also well known for its stoneflies.

Fig. 1.15. Fred Kirchner, Huntington, West Virginia stonefly specialist, hand picks emerging *Oemopteryx* adults from the Little Pigeon River, Tennessee.

Fig. 1.16. Dean Tanner, Mississippi College Biology student collects *Megarcys* and *Yoraperla* nymphs from upper Rock Creek in the Beartooth Pass area of Montana.

STONEFLY CLASSIFICATION AND IDENTIFICATION

All North American stoneflies are placed in the suborder Arctoperlaria, but nine families placed in two groups are recognized. The Systellognatha family group includes mostly larger species with a reduced basal tarsal segment. Two families in this group, Pteronarcyidae and Peltoperlidae have similar nymphal mouthparts which permit them to utilize leaf litter as a major food resource, whereas nymphs of Chloroperlidae, Perlodidae and Perlidae tend to be carnivorous. Adults of systellognathan families usually emerge in spring or summer.

Euholognatha includes four families of stoneflies whose members are typically small species with a long basal tarsal segment. Nymphs feed on detritus, leaf litter or algae which grows on the stream bottom. Leuctridae, Nemouridae and some Taeniopterygidae adults have one-segmented cerci. Members of these families are often part of the spring emerging fauna, but many winter, summer or fall emerging species are also included. Capniidae adults retain long, multisegmented cerci, and they are the classic "winter stoneflies" of North America.

The following pictorial keys should permit family identifications of North American stoneflies. Those who desire generic level identifications of nymphs are referred to Stewart and Stark (1988); Stewart and Harper (1996) includes generic level identification keys for nymphs and adults. No single volume exists for species level identifications of North American stoneflies, however, several useful taxonomic publications are included in the Bibliography section.

Fig. 1.17. *Paragnetina media* female with egg mass. WI: Portage Co., Tomorrow River, 8.vi.1990, S. Szczytko.

Fig. 1.18. *Beloneuria georgiana* mating pair. NC: Macon Co., Robin Branch, 21.v.1990, B. Stark, J. Parham, D. Tanner.

ADULT STONEFLY KEY

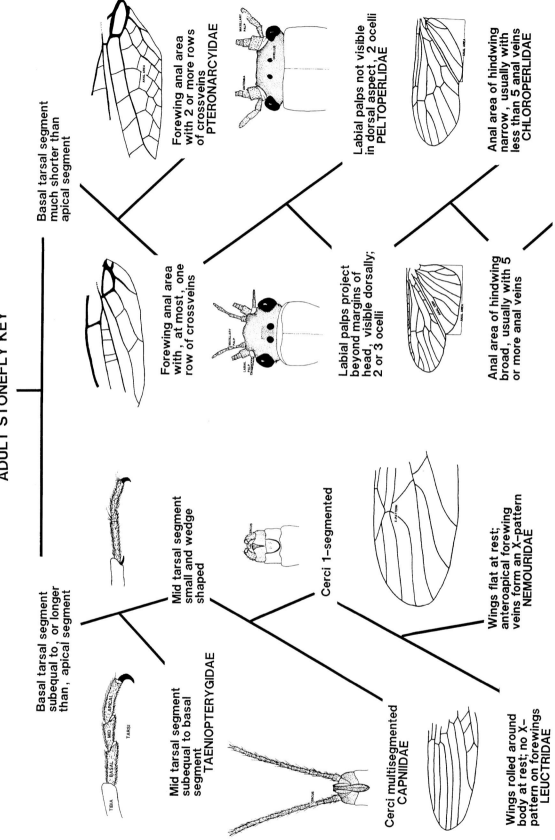

Basal tarsal segment much shorter than apical segment

Forewing anal area with 2 or more rows of crossveins
PTERONARCYIDAE

Forewing anal area with, at most, one row of crossveins

Labial palps not visible in dorsal aspect, 2 ocelli
PELTOPERLIDAE

Labial palps project beyond margins of head, visible dorsally; 2 or 3 ocelli

Anal area of hindwing narrow, usually with less than 5 anal veins
CHLOROPERLIDAE

Anal area of hindwing broad, usually with 5 or more anal veins

MAXILLARY PALP
OCELLUS
ANTENNA
ANAL AREA

MAXILLARY PALP
LABIAL PALP

ANAL AREA

Basal tarsal segment subequal to, or longer than, apical segment

Mid tarsal segment small and wedge shaped

Mid tarsal segment subequal to basal segment
TAENIOPTERYGIDAE

TIBIA
BASAL
MID
APICAL
TARSI

Cerci multisegmented
CAPNIIDAE

Cerci 1-segmented

CERCUS

Wings flat at rest; anteroapical forewing veins form an X-pattern
NEMOURIDAE

X-PATTERN

Wings rolled around body at rest; no X-pattern on forewings
LEUCTRIDAE

NYMPHAL STONEFLY KEY

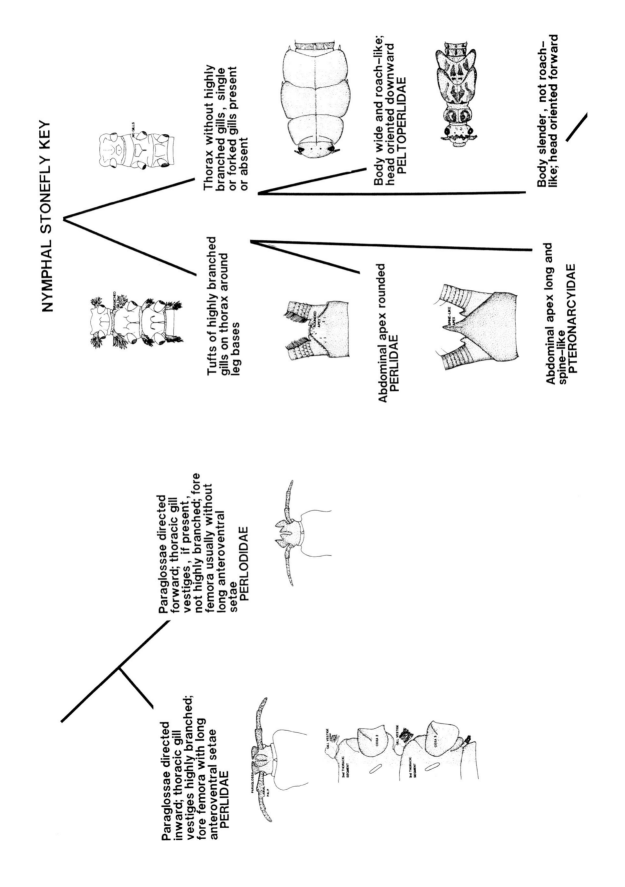

Thorax without highly branched gills, single or forked gills present or absent

Body wide and roach-like; head oriented downward
PELTOPERLIDAE

Body slender, not roach-like; head oriented forward

Tufts of highly branched gills on thorax around leg bases

Abdominal apex rounded
PERLIDAE

Abdominal apex long and spine-like
PTERONARCYIDAE

Paraglossae directed forward; thoracic gill vestiges, if present, not highly branched; fore femora usually without long anteroventral setae
PERLODIDAE

Paraglossae directed inward; thoracic gill vestiges highly branched; fore femora with long anteroventral setae
PERLIDAE

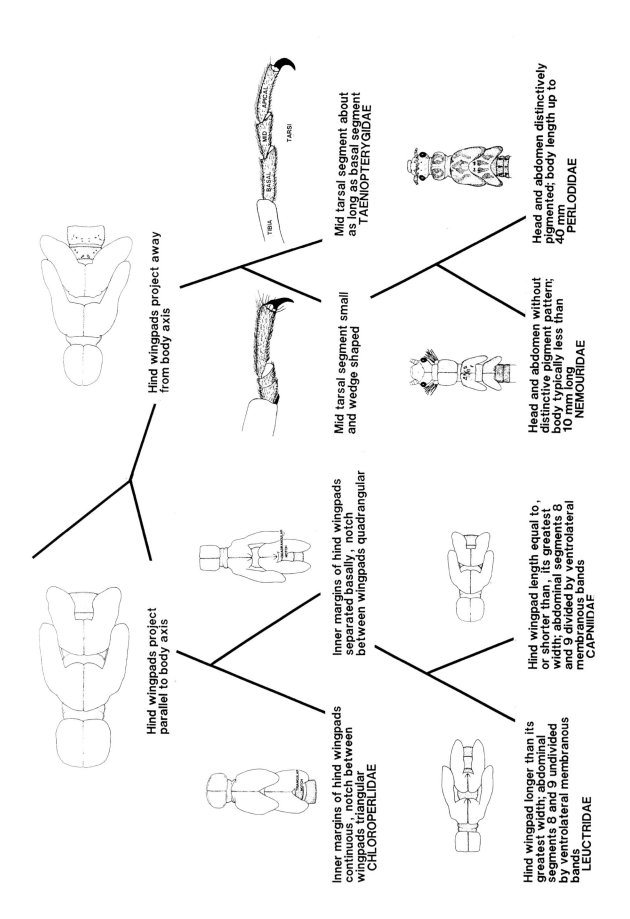

Hind wingpads project away
from body axis

TIBIA BASAL MID APICAL

TARSI

Mid tarsal segment about
as long as basal segment
TAENIOPTERYGIDAE

Mid tarsal segment small
and wedge shaped

Head and abdomen distinctively
pigmented; body length up to
40 mm
PERLODIDAE

Head and abdomen without
distinctive pigment pattern;
body typically less than
10 mm long
NEMOURIDAE

Hind wingpads project
parallel to body axis

QUADRANGULAR
NOTCH

Inner margins of hind wingpads
separated basally, notch
between wingpads quadrangular

TRIANGULAR
NOTCH

Inner margins of hind wingpads
continuous, notch between
wingpads triangular
CHLOROPERLIDAE

Hind wingpad length equal to,
or shorter than, its greatest
width; abdominal segments 8
and 9 divided by ventrolateral
membranous bands
CAPNIIDAE

Hind wingpad longer than its
greatest width; abdominal
segments 8 and 9 undivided
by ventrolateral membranous
bands
LEUCTRIDAE

12

Table 1. List of North American Families and Genera of Stoneflies. Numbers of described North American species are given for each genus, and primary distributions are given as "E" for eastern, "W" for western and "N" for northern.

Capniidae

	Allocapnia	41 species	E
	Bolshecapnia	6 species	W
	Capnia	52 species	W, N
	Capnura	7 species	W, N
	Eucapnopsis	1 species	W
	Isocapnia	11 species	W
	Mesocapnia	15 species	W
	Nemocapnia	1 species	E
	Paracapnia	5 species	E, W
	Utacapnia	11 species	W, N

Leuctridae

	Calileuctra	2 species	W
	Despaxia	1 species	W
	Leuctra	26 species	E
	Megaleuctra	6 species	E, W
	Moselia	1 species	W
	Paraleuctra	9 species	W, E
	Perlomyia	2 species	W
	Zealeuctra	8 species	E

Nemouridae

	Amphinemura	16 species	E, W
	Lednia	1 species	W
	Malenka	11 species	W
	Nemoura	5 species	W, N
	Ostrocerca	6 species	E, W
	Paranemoura	2 species	E
	Podmosta	5 species	W, N
	Prostoia	4 species	E, W
	Shipsa	1 species	E
	Soyedina	9 species	E, W
	Visoka	1 species	W
	Zapada	10 species	W, E

Taeniopterygidae

	Bolotoperla	1 species	E
	Doddsia	1 species	W
	Oemopteryx	4 species	E, W
	Strophopteryx	6 species	E
	Taenionema	12 species	W, E
	Taeniopteryx	11 species	E, W

Chloroperlidae

	Alaskaperla	1 species	W
	Alloperla	29 species	E, W
	Bisancora	2 species	W
	Haploperla	4 species	E, W
	Kathroperla	2 species	W
	Neaviperla	1 species	W
	Paraperla	2 species	W
	Plumiperla	2 species	W
	Rasvena	1 species	E
	Suwallia	6 species	W, E
	Sweltsa	27 species	W, E
	Triznaka	2 species	W
	Utaperla	2 species	W, E

Peltoperlidae

	Peltoperla	2 species	E
	Sierraperla	1 species	W
	Soliperla	6 species	W
	Tallaperla	6 species	E
	Viehoperla	1 species	E
	Yoraperla	4 species	W

Perlidae

	Acroneuria	15 species	E, W
	Agnetina	3 species	E
	Anacroneuria	2 species	W
	Attaneuria	1 species	E
	Beloneuria	3 species	E
	Calineuria	1 species	W
	Claassenia	1 species	W, N
	Doroneuria	2 species	W
	Eccoptura	1 species	E
	Hansonoperla	3 species	E
	Hesperoperla	2 species	W
	Neoperla	14 species	E, W
	Paragnetina	5 species	E
	Perlesta	14 species	E, W
	Perlinella	3 species	E

Perlodidae

	Arcynopteryx	1 species	W, N
	Baumannella	1 species	W
	Calliperla	1 species	W
	Cascadoperla	1 species	W
	Chernokrilus	2 species	W
	Clioperla	1 species	E
	Cosumnoperla	1 species	W
	Cultus	6 species	E, W
	Diploperla	4 species	E
	Diura	3 species	W, E
	Frisonia	1 species	W
	Helopicus	3 species	E
	Hydroperla	4 species	E
	Isogenoides	9 species	E, W
	Isoperla	57 species	E, W
	Kogotus	2 species	W
	Malirekus	2 species	E
	Megarcys	5 species	W
	Oconoperla	1 species	E
	Oroperla	1 species	W
	Osobenus	1 species	W
	Perlinodes	1 species	W
	Pictetiella	1 species	W
	Remenus	3 species	E
	Rickera	1 species	W
	Salmoperla	1 species	W
	Setvena	3 species	W
	Skwala	2 species	W
	Susulus	1 species	W
	Yugus	2 species	E

Pteronarcyidae

	Pteronarcella	2 species	W
	Pteronarcys	8 species	E, W

CHAPTER 2

STONEFLIES AND TROUT

Stoneflies are somewhat a mystery to many beginning trout fishers because their emergence behavior and day time activity are relatively cryptic. They certainly are not as well known as the mayflies (Ephemeroptera), caddisflies (Trichoptera) or true flies (Diptera) as popular fly patterns. Stoneflies probably are best known to trout fishers through the giant salmonfly (*Pteronarcys californica*) hatches on such western rivers as the Big Hole, Deschutes, Henry's Fork and Madison. A close relative, *P. dorsata*, also produces good hatches on the midwestern Au Sable, Rouge and Pere Marquette Rivers. These flies are gargantuan (ca. 2 inches) by most other aquatic insect standards and their sudden, mass availability creates a wanton, feeding frenzy among the largest trout. The salmonfly hatch is well documented in fly fishing literature and there currently are more fly patterns available for salmonfly nymphs and adults than for any other stonefly.

In North America, the stonefly fauna is divided geographically into eastern and western elements. These faunal elements are distinct with the front range of the Rocky Mountains serving as the approximate boundary. There are only a few truly transcontinental species and they are limited to the northern areas of the continent. The Great Plains serves as the mixing zone, and in the Dakotas, Wyoming, Nebraska and eastern Colorado several representatives from both eastern and western faunal elements can be collected. Thus, the generic name applied to a local hatch may be the same as that in another geographic area, but the species are likely to be different. This often requires a size or color difference, or use of a different material, when constructing a fly to match hatches from different geographic areas. Good examples of this diversity are provided by the mayfly genus *Ephemerella*, the stonefly genus *Isoperla*, and the caddisfly genus *Hydropsyche*. Each of these genera have numerous eastern and western species found commonly in trout streams. The fly fisher can use the same general pattern for these insects but vary the size, color and materials used in constructing the fly. This greatly reduces the number of patterns a fisher needs to learn, and provides a variety of flies that are effective in many areas on the continent.

The perception of many fishers is that stoneflies are coincidental with, and limited to, high quality trout streams with cold temperatures, fast flows and high oxygen levels. This perception is supported by numerous studies indicating stoneflies as a group are among the most pollution intolerant of all aquatic insects in North America. Generally, any stream with conditions favorable to sustain trout, also will support stoneflies. Most of the larger western trout rivers and small southern Appalachian and Cascade Mountain streams support at least 25 stonefly species. Stoneflies may be the dominant invertebrate predator in many trout streams, however there also are many species found in slower moving, sluggish streams with accumulated debris and silt.

The importance of stoneflies, mayflies, caddisflies and midges in the diet of trout is well known. Stoneflies can be of prime importance to trout because they usually are among the largest, consistently available, food items in trout streams. The aquatic nymphal stage comprises the longest period in the life cycle of stoneflies. Most of the medium size species have an eight or nine month aquatic nymphal stage and a relatively short lived terrestrial adult stage. The larger species of Perlidae and Pteronarcyidae typically have life cycles greater than one year (often 2 or 3 years), and have two or three cohorts of nymphs available in the stream at any time. These insects provide food for trout throughout the entire year, and also offer different sizes from which to select. Most other stonefly species have life cycles of one year and provide variable periods of food availability. These species may be important in the diet of trout only when they are abundant and larger. Evidence of trout feeding on nymphs ("nymphing") can be seen by the side flashing of fish as they try to "nose out" prey items in riffles. Trout fishers who notice this activity can take advantage of fish by using an appropriate nymph pattern. Because trout are cold blooded animals their feeding activity and metabolism typically slows through the colder months and also when summer temperatures reach a near critical maximum in thermally marginal streams. Contrary to popular perception, trout actually do feed during the winter, however they may feed less due to the reduction in metabolic rate.

NYMPH BEHAVIOR

Knowledge of stonefly ecology and behavior are important components for success in fishing stonefly patterns. Nymph fishing can be productive at virtually any time of the year because nymphs are continuously available in most trout streams. Stoneflies with one year life cycles often hatch in late summer or early fall and are at their smallest at this time. Rapid nymphal growth usually follows hatching until water temperatures drop during the winter months. This slow winter growth is followed by a dramatic increase in growth as water temperatures increase in the spring. What this means to the fly fisher is that during the course of a year, several sizes of nymphs will be needed to match the nymphs in the stream, and that the larger sizes are usually needed during the spring and early summer. However, size of the nymphal pattern is not usually as critical as it may be for the adult pattern because there is a natural spread (1-3 hook sizes) of different size nymphs in the stream at a given time. In stoneflies with a two or three year life cycle, there are many nymph sizes present at any time, but each cohort usually is a distinct size class. As nymphs grow they periodically shed their outer skin (exoskeleton). This process, called molting, results in nymphs that are very soft and white or cream colored. This condition persists for several hours until the exoskeleton hardens and color patterns develop. Molting often occurs at night or during the early morning hours, however it is not uncommon to find these "albino" nymphs in samples taken in later morning. Several fly patterns have been developed to imitate this freshly molted condition in nymphs of perlids and perlodids. It is recommended that they be fished during the morning hours.

DRIFT

The natural movements of nymphs are important in deciding how and when to properly fish a particular pattern. Many aquatic insect species exhibit a distinctive downstream movement known as "drift". Drifting insects are suspended in the current and as they are swept downstream, they are quite vulnerable to predation. Many stoneflies, especially the strong clingers such as *Acroneuria* and other Systellognatha, do not exhibit strong drift patterns, whereas weak clingers such as *Amphinemura* and *Prostoia* are sometimes common in drift. Drift is related to catastrophic events such as spates, extreme thermal changes or discharges of pollutants, and to behavioral events caused by competition, predation or life history phenomena. The numbers of insects drifting over a riffle during a 24 hour period can greatly exceed the resident population, and the drift volume may vary seasonally or daily. Behavioral drift, or "voluntary drift," usually peaks at, or just after sunset, and a secondary peak may occur just before sunrise, or at another time depending on the species. Experimental results suggest this behavior is related to light intensity; in fact, the drift volume is lower during full moon than on dark nights. This behavior and activity levels are important to feeding trout and ultimately to the trout fisher. Many trout fishers have witnessed the increased feeding activity of trout during the pre- and post-sunset periods. During this time it is important to fish stonefly nymph patterns suspended in the current in order to imitate drift behavior and posture. Many nymph patterns use a curved hook to better imitate the naturally curved body form of a drifting nymph. Fishing these patterns can be especially productive during the spring and summer when drift rates are at their highest.

EMERGENCE BEHAVIOR

Emergence is another important consideration for the trout fisher. This activity involves the transformation of the aquatic nymph into a winged, terrestrial adult. Stoneflies differ from most other aquatic insects because they do not emerge from the water surface, rather they crawl out of the water onto the bank, or onto objects protruding from the water to complete their final molt. Prior to emergence many species migrate toward the stream margins, or congregate near objects protruding from the water surface, in a "staging" activity as they wait for environmental cues to stimulate emergence. In some species such as *Pteronarcys dorsata*, pre-emergent nymphs may crawl a considerable distance from the stream to emerge. We have observed emerging nymphs of this species crawl more than 20 meters from the stream, and then up to four meters high on trees before molting. Other aquatic insects, like the mayflies and caddisflies, offer excellent fishing during their emergence period. This is because the pre-emergent nymphs and pupae usually struggle at the water surface to escape the exoskeleton and this makes them very vulnerable to feeding trout. One of the most famous and productive hatches in the midwest involves the mayfly, *Hexagenia limbata* (Michigan Caddis, Michigan Giant). The nymph of this species rises to the surface and molts to the subimago, or dun stage. The struggle at the surface creates a disturbance that attracts trout. Unfortunately emerging stoneflies do not exhibit this type of behavior. Nevertheless, shed exoskeletons, or "shucks" can provide an important guide for fishers who want to know what hatch is in progress on their favorite trout stream. These shucks remain on protruding objects, or bankside vegetation, until high water sweeps them away; thus they can provide a chronological sequence for the progression of hatches through the season.

HATCHES

Hatches usually are influenced by temperature and photoperiod. Temperature usually is the more important cue except in spring habitat where water temperatures often are uniform. Emergence may be stimulated by a specific temperature, or by the accumulation of degree days (average daily temperatures) over the life cycle period. Because of annual differences in water temperature, hatches do not always occur at the same date on a given stream. During warm years, hatches occur earlier than in cold years. Emergence calendars often give a one or two week "window" of time when the hatch is expected. It is not uncommon to find hatches of a stonefly species offset within, or between, streams depending on the local thermal regime. In Wisconsin, many of the perlodid and perlid stoneflies begin hatching a week or two earlier in southern streams than in northern streams. This difference is even greater for streams with great latitudinal or elevational differences.

In most trout streams, particularly those in mountainous regions, there is a marked upstream progression of the hatch. The upstream progression of the Madison River, Montana, salmonfly hatch is so well documented that many sport shops and newspapers give daily reports on the location of the hatch. It is prudent for the trout fisher to be on the reach of the river where the hatch has just begun because fishing is enhanced during the early days of the hatch when trout are more agressive and hungry. Trout continue to feed during a heavy hatch until they are satiated. We have seen trout stomachs literally packed with *Hexagenia limbata* during the first days of that hatch. After feeding so intensively in such a short period of time, several days may be required before the contents of their distended stomachs are digested. During this time many trout stop feeding, or feed at reduced levels.

Winter Hatches: Stoneflies are unusual among aquatic insects because there are many winter emerging species. Members of the family Capniidae, and some species of other Euholognathan families, emerge in winter. Most of these species emerge during the day when air temperatures are greatest. The capniids, or tiny winter blacks, as fly fishers call them, are the most common winter emerging group. It is not unusual to find these stoneflies walking about on snow or ice in January or February when air temperatures are hovering near the freezing point. They are sometimes mistaken for ants because they are small (ca. 3-5 mm), dark bodied, and may have the wings reduced or absent. These stoneflies generally are insignificant to fly fishers because fishing seasons are closed in most areas when they emerge. The common genera in eastern North America are *Allocapnia* and *Paracapnia*, whereas *Capnia* is the most common capniid genus in much of western North America. The nemourid stoneflies emerge somewhat later than capniids and are larger and lighter in color. *Amphinemura* and *Nemoura* are two of the more important hatches. Leuctridae also have minor value to fly fishers because they usually are less abundant than capniids and nemourids on trout streams. *Leuctra* is the most common and widespread eastern genus and *Paraleuctra* is most common in the west. Leuctrids resemble capniids but they are more slender and have short, 1-segmented tails, or cerci.

Early Spring Hatches: Taeniopterygid stoneflies provide the most important early spring hatch. These stoneflies are larger than the winter blacks, and in many areas their emergence coincides with the fishing season. Emergence of taeniopterygids can begin as early as December in the southern United States, but on northern streams they provide a significant March hatch. *Taeniopteryx* is the most common eastern genus and *Taenionema* is most common in the west. *Taeniopteryx nivalis* is perhaps the most important early spring hatch in the east; *Strophopteryx fasciata*, another eastern species, is less common but can provide excellent fishing in streams where it is abundant. *Taeniopteryx* is a dark brown fly with mottled wings, and *Strophopteryx* typically is one hook size smaller, and pale brown with a slight reddish hue.

Mid-to-Late Spring Hatches: During mid-spring, stonefly hatches really accelerate, but no single family is dominant. Perlodidae, Pteronarcyidae, Chloroperlidae and Peltoperlidae are probably the most important contributors to hatches in this period, but the famous salmonfly hatches certainly dominate the fly fishing literature. In addition to the giant salmonflies, the small salmonflies of genus *Pteronarcella* are important on many western rivers. These stoneflies are much smaller than *Pteronarcys*, but often they are more abundant. At times their preiminence can cause trout to "switch" from *Pteronarcys* patterns even though the hatch of giant salmonflies is still in progress.

Isoperla is the most important perlodid genus because it is diverse, abundant in trout streams, and has a transcontinental distribution. However, several other genera including *Isogenoides* and *Cultus* certainly are of major importance on both eastern and western trout streams. *Isogenoides olivaceus* is a common model for eastern and midwestern streams, but *I. zionensis* and other relatives are abundant late spring emergers in western rivers like the Pecos (New Mexico), Gunnison (Colorado), and Green (Utah). *Cultus* species (e.g., *C. tostonus*, *C. decisus*) are smaller than *Isogenoides* and may be imitated with dark *Isoperla* patterns. Some *Isoperla* species are called "yellow sallies" but in such a large genus considerable variation occurs. In the western states *Isoperla mormona* (the "mormon girl") and *I. quinquepunctata* have a distinctly reddish cast to the abdomen, and dark brown species like *I. fulva* also abound in trout waters of this region.

Nymphal peltoperlids may be less significant than these other groups in the diets of trout because their usual microdistribution in leaf litter and headwater streams might make them less available. Sheer numbers, however, would seem to dictate their importance, particularly during the hatch. In some Appalachian streams, hundreds of *Tallaperla* or *Peltoperla* nymphs occur per square meter, and similar densities of *Yoraperla* and *Sierraperla* are known for some locations in the Sierras and Cascades. We are unaware of popular fly patterns tied to specifically imitate peltoperlids, but because they are robust, and distinctive in size and coloration, they should make excellent models for spring hatches.

Nymphs of most chloroperlid genera burrow deeply in the substrate and thus, are unimportant for trout. The adults, however, are often present in large numbers and their oviposition flights at dusk can be quite impressive. Hatches of "little green" species like *Alloperla imbecilla*, *A. atlantica* and *A. usa*, and "little yellow" species like *Haploperla brevis* and *Sweltsa mediana* are significant in many eastern streams, but in the west and northeast this group emerges primarily during the summer.

Summer Hatches: The June through August hatch period is dominated in most areas by species of Perlidae, Perlodidae and Chloroperlidae. Large perlids of *Acroneuria*, *Calineuria*, *Claassenia*, *Hesperoperla* and other genera comprise the "big golden" complex. Big golden, or golden stone patterns may rival the salmonfly patterns in popularity and utility, however these insects seldom occur in the numbers achieved by salmonflies. Trout streams throughout the western mountains typically support good populations of *Hesperoperla pacifica*. This large, golden brown stone occurs in both short winged and long winged forms, and often the species is abundant in large springs. *Calineuria californica*, superficially similar to *Hesperoperla*, occurs in trout streams from California to Montana. In many smaller streams in this region another large, but dark brown perlid, genus *Doroneuria*, occurs. *Doroneuria* males are short winged, but the large, heavy bodied females have long wings. *Claassenia*, the other common western perlid, also shares these wing conditions. *Claassenia* is a stonefly of large rivers such as the Yellowstone, and it is particularly common in the Rocky Mountains. An interesting aspect of this stonefly is the ability of the short winged males to "walk on water". As darkness approaches, *Claassenia* males emerge from their daytime hiding places, scurry over the water surface, and seek out females as they emerge on rocks.

Noteworthy eastern golden brown hatches include several species of *Acroneuria* (e.g., *A. lycorias*, *A. abnormis*, *A. carolinensis*), *Agnetina* (e.g., *A. capitata*, *A. flavescens*), and *Paragnetina* (e.g., *P. media*, *P. immarginata*). Most of these species are brown to dark brown and more than one inch in length. *P. media* is perhaps the most important of these stones in midwestern trout streams, but *A. carolinensis* and *A. abnormis* are dominant in the central and southern Appalachians. The importance of *P. immarginata* is due primarily to its late summer hatch in Appalachian streams.

In addition to the golden stones and medium brown patterns used to match perlid and perlodid summer hatches, some consideration should be given to the chloroperlids, particularly in the west. Most of these summer emerging chloroperlids of western trout streams are pale yellow or green, slender bodied stoneflies. Several species of *Triznaka*, *Suwallia*, *Sweltsa* and *Alloperla* have particularly large hatches in Rocky Mountain and Sierra streams. *Sweltsa* species (e.g., *S. coloradensis*, *S. pacifica*, *S. revelstoka*) generally are more robust than these other chloroperlids and bear a general similarity to "yellow sally" *Isoperla* types. Several popular "little yellow" and "little green" patterns are excellent imitations of *Suwallia* (e.g., *S. pallidula*, *S. autumna*) and *Alloperla* (e.g., *A. severa*, *A. delicata*) species.

ESTABLISHED STONEFLY PATTERNS

The following list of traditional stonefly patterns has been gleaned from Schwiebert (1973) and Richards, et al. (1980). Specific instructions for tying many of these and other patterns are available in Richards, et al.

NYMPHAL PATTERNS

PATTERN	MODEL	PRIMARY DISTRIBUTION
Giant Black Stonefly	*Pteronarcys dorsata*	Eastern (E)
Giant Salmonfly	*Pteronarcys californica*	Western (W)
Bird's Stone	*Pteronarcys*	E or W
Bitch Creek	*Pteronarcys*	E or W
Ted's Stonefly	*Pteronarcys*	E or W
Golden Stone	*Calineuria* or *Hesperoperla*	W
	Acroneuria, Agnetina or *Paragnetina*	E
Keel Stonefly	*Calineuria* or *Hesperoperla*	W
	Acroneuria, Agnetina or *Paragnetina*	E
Brown Willowfly	*Hesperoperla pacifica*	W
Orange Stonefly	*Paragnetina immarginata*	E
Great Stonefly	*Agnetina capitata*	E
Great Brown Stonefly	*Acroneuria lycorias*	E
Little Red Stonefly	*Strophopteryx fasciata*	E
Little Yellow Stonefly	*Isoperla bilineata*	E
Western Yellow Stonefly	*Isoperla mormona*	W
Mormon Girl	*Isoperla mormona*	W
Light Brown Stonefly	*Isoperla signata*	E
Little Sepia Stonefly	*Zapada cinctipes*	W
Little Western Stonefly	*Malenka californica*	W
Early Brown Stonefly	*Taeniopteryx nivalis*	E
Early Black Stonefly	*Taeniopteryx nivalis*	E
Medium Brown Stonefly	*Isogenoides olivaceus*	E

ADULT PATTERNS

PATTERN	MODEL	PRIMARY DISTRIBUTION
Salmonfly Adult	*Pteronarcys* or *Pteronarcella*	E or W
Sofa Pillow	*Pteronarcys*	E or W
Bird's Stonefly	generic	E or W
Extended Body Stone	generic	E or W
Big Golden Stone	*Calineuria* or *Hesperoperla*	W
	Acroneuria, Agnetina or *Paragnetina*	E
Bitterroot Stonefly	*Hesperoperla pacifica*	W
Little Green Stonefly	generic chloroperlid	E or W
Little Yellow Stonefly	generic chloroperlid	E or W
Medium Brown Adult	*Isogenoides olivaceus*	E
Tiny Winter Black	generic capniid	E or W
Early Spring Brown Adult	*Taeniopteryx nivalis*	E

Fig. 2.1. Atlantic Salmon Golden Stonefly pattern (tied by J. Dimick).

Fig. 2.2. Extended Body Stonefly pattern (tied by J. Dimick).

Fig. 2.3. *Claassenia* Nymph pattern (tied by J. Dimick).

Fig. 2.4. Little Yellow Nymph pattern (tied by J. Dimick).

Fig. 2.5. Medium Brown Nymph pattern (tied by J. Dimick).

Fig. 2.6. Early Brown Nymph pattern (tied by J. Dimick).

CHAPTER 3

FAMILY PTERONARCYIDAE—THE SALMONFLIES

Most salmonflies are large, grey to dark brown or black insects with numerous apical crossveins in their wings and many species have a salmon colored pigment in the soft areas surrounding the first thoracic segment. The dark brown nymphs have highly branched gills on the ventral surface of each thoracic segment, and on the first two or three abdominal segments. The nymphal abdomen terminates in a short spine-like process. Many streams support large populations of salmonflies, and in these, their emergence and oviposition activity can be quite spectacular. Emergences of *Pteronarcys californica* are routinely reported in the sports pages of many western North American newspapers, and many popular flies are modeled after members of this family (Table 3.1). Currently two genera and ten species of pteronarcyids are recognized in North America.

Table 3.1. Selected flies modeled after Pteronarcyid stoneflies (after Leiser and Boyle, 1982).

Fly Name	Model	Creator
Catskill Curler	*Pteronarcys* sp.	M. Vinciguerra
Curved Dorsata Nymph	*P. dorsata*	J. Neve and D. Fox
Don's Brown Stonefly Nymph	*P. dorsata*	J. Neve and D. Fox
Polar Commander	*P. dorsata*	J. Neve and D. Fox
K's Butt Salmonfly	*P. californica*	R. Boyle

Genus *Pteronarcys*

Eight species of giant salmonflies occur in North America; six of these are distributed primarily in the east, and two occur only in the west. Species are usually distinguished by examination of male and female genitalic characteristics. Nymphs of the genus have gills on abdominal segments 1 and 2 and adults are easily recognized by their large size and abundant crossveins in the forewing anal area.

Pteronarcys californica Newport

Adult length 2-3 inches. Distribution western North America from Alaska to New Mexico and Californica. Locally very common in large to medium sized rivers at lower elevations. The range of *P. californica* broadly overlaps those of two other large salmonfly species, *P. dorsata* and *P. princeps*.

P. princeps is a darker species typically found in small streams from southwestern British Columbia to California and in isolated mountain ranges of Nevada, eastern Oregon and western Utah. *P. dorsata* resembles *P. californica* in general coloration, but the ninth abdominal sternum of *P. dorsata* males projects over the tenth and is notched on the posterior margin. In the Rocky Mountains, *P. dorsata* is usually found in the Mississippi-Missouri drainage basin. Baumann et al. (1977) includes a key to nymphs and adults of these three species.

Emergence is recorded from April to June.

[Clockwise from upper left]

Fig. 3.1 *Pteronarcys californica* female. OR: Multnomah Co., Wahkeena Falls, 5.vi.1991, B. Stark, R. Baumann, and C. Henderson.

Fig. 3.2 *Pteronarcys dorsata* nymph. WI: Oconto Co., S. Branch Oconto River, 16.v.1990. S. Sczcytko.

Fig. 3.3 *Pteronarcys dorsata* female. MS: Simpson Co., Rials Creek, 5.ii.1992, B. Stark.

Pteronarcys dorsata (Say)

Adult length 1.5-2.5 inches. Distribution transcontinental, in eastern North America from Labrador and Manitoba to Florida and Louisiana, in the west, scattered populations have been reported from Kansas to Alaska. In the east, the range of *P. dorsata* broadly overlaps those of five other large salmonflies.

Pteronarcys biloba, *P. comstocki*, *P. proteus* and *P. scotti* are primarily Appalachian stoneflies whose nymphs bear lateral knobs or spines on, at least some, abdominal segments and whose males do not have the ninth abdominal sternum prolonged and notched. *P. pictetii*, which occurs with *P. dorsata* in the upper midwest and Great Lakes region, shares the modified ninth abdominal sternum character with *P. dorsata*, but in *P. pictetii*, this structure is also curved downward near the apex.

Emergence begins in February in Mississippi and continues through June in upper midwestern states.

Pteronarcys scotti Ricker

Adult length 1.5-2.5 inches. Distribution eastern North America from Pennsylvania to Georgia along the Appalachians. Common in third order streams of the Blue Ridge and Ridge and Valley provinces. *P. scotti* is most similar to *P. biloba*, *P. comstocki* and *P. proteus* and can be reliably separated from these species only through close examination of male and female genitalic characters. Hitchcock (1974) includes a key to eastern *Pteronarcys* species other than *P. scotti*.

Emergence occurs from April to June.

Fig. 3.4 *Pteronarcys scotti* female. NC, Jackson Co., Mull Creek, 26.v.1993, B. Stark, D. Kelly, and R. Simmons

Genus *Pteronarcella*

Two species of small salmonflies, *P. badia* and *P. regularis* occur in the western third of the United States and Canada. The nymphs of these resemble small *Pteronarcys* but the presence of gills on abdominal segment III readily distinguishes *Pteronarcella* from the giant salmonflies, and the adults are about half the size of *Pteronarcys*. Baumann et al. (1977) includes keys to these species.

Pteronarcella badia (Hagen)

Adult length 0.75-1.0 inches. Distribution western North America from southern Alberta and British Columbia to Arizona and New Mexico. Locally very common in streams at lower elevations.

Males often have shortened wings which reveal the curious U-shaped dorsal lobe on abdominal segment IX. Adults have a dark brown body color and the wings are generally similar to those of *Pteronarcys* in bearing many crossveins. *P. regularis* is very similar but is apparently restricted to the Coast, Cascade and Sierra Nevada Mountains.

Emergence in the Rocky Mountains is recorded from May through July.

Fig. 3.5. *Pteronarcella badia* nymph, ventral aspect. CO: Jackson Co., Michigan River, 19.v.1991, C. R. Nelson.

Fig. 3.6 *Pteronarcella badia* male. CO: Boulder Co., Boulder Creek, v.1995. B. Kondratieff.

CHAPTER 4

FAMILY PELTOPERLIDAE—THE ROACHFLIES

Roachflies are small to medium size stoneflies ranging in color from pale yellow to dark brown. Nymphs are usually brown, without distinctive patterns and they bear simple or forked gills on the thorax near the coxal bases. The three thoracic sternal plates are large and typically overlap one another. Adults have short, relatively wide heads from which the maxillary palpi project; the labial palps are short and do not project beyond the margins of the head. All North American peltoperlids posess only two ocelli.

Roachflies are noted leaf shredders and their densities are at times quite impressive, particularly in small Appalachian headwater streams. Several species are common in splash zones and small spring seeps. Twenty species placed in six genera occur in North America.

Genus *Peltoperla*

Two species of these brown roachflies, *P. arcuata* and *P. tarteri* are known. Both are species of springbrooks and their ranges broadly overlap in the Blue Ridge, Ridge and Valley, and Appalachian Plateau provinces of Virginia and West Virginia, however, *P. arcuata* occurs as far north as New York while *P. tarteri* appears to have a more restricted distribution. Males of this group are distinctive by virtue of their slender, sclerotized epiprocts and the females are recognized by their relatively large subgenital plates. Stark and Kondratieff (1987) provide illustrations which permit separation of these species.

Peltoperla arcuata Needham

Adult length 0.5-0.7 inches. Distribution New York to Kentucky and Virginia. Males of these dark brown roachflies are easily separated from other eastern peltoperlids by the basally curved cerci, however nymphs are difficult to separate from *Tallaperla* nymphs and females are distinguished from those of *P. tarteri* only by careful examination of subgenital plate and vaginal sclerite shape.

Emergence is recorded from May through July.

Fig. 4.1. *Peltoperla arcuata* male. WV: Mingo Co., Laurel Fork, 27.v.1993, B. Kondratieff, F. Kirchner.

Fig. 4.2. *Sierraperla cora* female. CA: Plumas Co., Domingo Springs, 30.v.1991, B. Stark, R. Baumann, C. Henderson.

Genus *Sierraperla*

Only one species of large roachfly, *S. cora*, is known. Nymphs are common on wood and rocks in splash zones of springs such as those forming the Sacramento River headwaters near Mt. Shasta. The nymphs are quite distinctive with curled and forked finger-like gills, and a pointed, pteronarcyid-like abdominal apex. Adults are larger than other peltoperlids and have short, 10 or 11-segmented cerci which lack long ventral setae. Males have poorly developed paraprocts and an indistinct epiproct, but the ninth sternum bears a wide, oval vesicle.

Sierraperla cora (Needham and Smith)

Adult length 0.8-1.3 inches. Distribution northern Sierras and Coastal Ranges of California and southern Oregon. The species was named from a specimen listed from Reno, but no extant populations have been discovered in Nevada. *S. cora* is very abundant in large springs of the northern Sierras. In streams originating from these springs, ovipositing females almost certainly are an important part of the diet of local trout populations.

Emergence is recorded from May to July.

Genus *Soliperla*

Six species of these pale brown roachflies occur from central California to Washington, usually associated with splash zones and spring seeps. *S. fenderi*, the northern-most species occurs on Mt. Rainier and Mt. Adams, *S. tillamook* is found on the northwestern Oregon Coastal Range, *S. campanula* occurs from Mt. Hood through the central Oregon Cascades, *S. quadrispinula* occurs along the Coastal Range of northern California and Oregon, *S. sierra* is known from a few localities in the Sierras of northern California and *S. thyra* is common in the Coastal Range and Napa Valley area north of San Francisco. Adults of most species are pale yellow brown with a distinctive median dark stripe on the prothorax and the robust nymphs have pale spots on several anterior abdominal segments which give them a distinctive appearance. Species keys are given in Stark (1983).

Soliperla campanula (Jewett)

Adult length 0.6-0.8 inches. Distribution Oregon Cascades from Mt. Hood to the Three Sisters area. Very common in splash zones of tributary streams in the Columbia River Gorge and on Mt. Hood. *S. campanula* males are distinguished by a row of short, peg-like setae on the midventral surface of the internal genitalia, but females cannot be separated from other *Soliperla* with certainty.

Emergence is recorded from May to July.

Fig. 4.3. *Soliperla campanula* female. OR: Multnomah Co., Wahkeena Falls, 5.vi.1991, B. Stark, R. Baumann, C. Henderson.

Fig. 4.4. *Soliperla fenderi* male. WN: Skamania Co., tributary East Canyon Creek, Mt. Adams, 7.vi.1991, B. Stark, R. Baumann, C. Henderson.

Soliperla fenderi (Jewett)

Adult length 0.6-0.8 inches. Distribution Cascades of central Washington from Mt. Rainier to Mt. Adams. Nymphs occur in small spring seeps which enter streams such as St. Andrews Creek on Mt. Rainier, but they are uncommon. *S. fenderi* males are distinguished by a row of long, thin setae lining the inner margins of the anteroventral lobes of the internal genitalia and females are the most distinctive in the genus with a V-shaped notch on the subgenital plate.

Emergence is recorded in June and July.

Genus *Tallaperla*

Six species of these brown roachflies occur along the Appalachians and into Florida and western Alabama. The brown or red-brown nymphs are often very abundant in leaf litter and dozens of individuals may scurry like rats from a handful of leaves lifted from the riffle area of a stream. Species of *Tallaperla* occur in a variety of streams ranging in size from spring seeps to rivers. Identification of species in this genus is more difficult than in other peltoperlid groups and may require careful study of eggs and genitalia. Stark (1983) presents keys to adults.

Tallaperla anna (Needham and Smith)

Adult length 0.5-0.7 inches. Distribution central and southern Appalachians from Virginia to South Carolina and Georgia. *T. anna* is a pale brown or yellowish species. Males have a narrow vesicle and females an unnotched subgenital plate. The species is most common in small creeks at higher elevations.

Emergence is recorded from May through June.

Fig. 4.5. *Tallaperla anna* male. NC: Haywood Co., North Fork Cove Creek, 23.v.1993, B. Kondratieff, F. Kirchner.

Fig. 4.6. *Tallaperla cornelia* mating pair. NC: Macon Co., Robin Branch, 21.v.1990, B. Stark, J. Parham, D. Tanner.

Tallaperla cornelia (Needham and Smith)

Adult length 0.5-0.7 inches. Distribution southern Appalachians, Piedmont and Coastal Plains from North Carolina to Florida and west to Alabama. *T. cornelia* is a brown species with a moderately wide, but basally constricted male vesicle.

Emergence is recorded from April to June.

Tallaperla laurie (Ricker)

Adult length 0.5-0.7 inches. Distribution southern Appalachians and Piedmont from South Carolina and Tennessee to Georgia. *T. laurie* is a pale brown species whose males exhibit broadly rounded paraproct apices. Females are distinctive by virtue of their narrowly notched subgenital plate. This species occurs in spring seeps and small creeks, usually at lower elevations.

Emergence is recorded from May to June.

Tallaperla maria (Needham and Smith)

Adult length 0.5-0.7 inches. Distribution New York to Georgia and South Carolina. Common in rivers and creeks along the Appalachians. *T. maria* is a brown species with a wide male vesicle and a slightly notched female subgenital plate.

Emergence is recorded from April through June.

[Clockwise from upper left]

Fig. 4.7. *Tallaperla laurie* male. GA: Murray Co., 29.v.1993, B. Stark, R. Simmons, D. Kelly.

Fig. 4.8. *Tallaperla laurie* nymph. GA: Murray Co., 29.v.1993, B. Stark, R. Simmons, D. Kelly.

Fig. 4.9. *Tallaperla maria* female. VA: Smyth Co., North Fork Holston River, 20.v.1993, B. Kondratieff, F. Kirchner.

Genus *Viehoperla*

Only one species of this small, pale roachfly genus is known, *V. ada*. Until the 1980's this was considered one of our rarest North American stoneflies, but good populations were discovered in tiny spring seeps and splash zones of small streams in the southern Appalachians, and the small, dark brown nymphs were described by Stark and Stewart (1982). Males of this group are easily recognized by virtue of their long epiproct and poorly developed paraprocts, but females might be confused with pale *Tallaperla* species. The slightly longer subgenital plate of *Viehoperla* permits reliable separation of these groups.

Fig. 4.10. *Viehoperla ada* female. NC: Macon Co., Robin Branch, 21.v.1990, B. Stark, J. Parham, D. Tanner.

Viehoperla ada (Needham and Smith)

Adult length 0.4-0.5 inches. Distribution mountains of Tennessee, Georgia and the Carolinas. *V. ada* is the smallest and palest adult peltoperlid known in eastern North America and the nymphs occur in the smallest of spring seeps. Emergence is recorded from May to July.

Genus *Yoraperla*

Four species of these dark brown western roachflies occur in California, the Pacific Northwest and northern Rocky Mountains. *Y. brevis* occurs in the northern Rockies, *Y. nigrisoma* throughout the Sierras and into the Cascades of Oregon and southern Washington and *Y. mariana* is a larger species of the Cascades and northern Sierras. The fourth species *Y. siletz* is known from Coastal Ranges of California and Oregon.

Nymphs generally occur in small creeks and they are sometimes quite abundant. Males have short, seven-segmented cerci and little development of the epiproct. Females have dark bar-like areas on the ninth abdominal sternum which project under the subgenital plate and their eggs are flattened and wafer-like. The dark brown nymphs bear rows of long setae on their femora.

Yoraperla nigrisoma (Banks)

Adult length 0.3-0.6 inches. Distribution Sierras and Cascades from Mt. Rainier to southern California; the species is particularly common in small creeks and springs of the Lake Tahoe region.

This species has been called *Y. brevis* for most of this century but Stark and Nelson (1994) found these species to be distinct. *Y. nigrisoma* males have a narrow, somewhat triangular shaped vesicle while other North American species have wider, oval shaped vesicles.

Emergence is recorded from April to July.

Fig. 4.11. *Yoraperla nigrisoma* female. CA: El Dorado Co., Tony Gulch, 11.v.1995, R. Bottorff.

CHAPTER 5

FAMILY PERLIDAE—THE STONES

Members of family Perlidae are medium size to large summer- emerging stoneflies which vary in color from pale yellow to black. Nymphs are typically predaceous and often are distinctively patterned in yellow and brown. Highly branched gills are located around the coxal bases and sometimes on the paraprocts in the anal region. Adults often retain remnants of these gills which help in distinguishing species of this group from those of Perlodidae.

Adults and nymphs of larger *Acroneuria*, *Agnetina*, *Calineuria*, and *Hesperoperla* species are common models for some of the artificial flies used for trout fishing. Although many unique names have been proposed for these creations, "golden stone" is often used for basic large perlid patterns. Fifteen genera and 70 perlid species are currently recognized in North America.

Genus *Acroneuria*

Fifteen species of these large golden stones occur primarily in eastern North America, but at least two species have crossed the Great Plains and occur in large western rivers such as the upper Green, Missouri, and Saskatchewan. Males have the paraprocts developed into genital hooks, and an oval hammer occurs on abdominal sternum IX. Most females have a moderately produced subgenital plate, and the eggs usually have a small button-like collar. In older literature, *Acroneuria* was used in a broad sense to include many large perlids which are now properly placed in other genera. Stark and Gaufin (1976) reviewed the genus but three new species have subsequently been described, and one other recent nomenclatural change involving *A. evoluta* is discussed below.

Acroneuria abnormis (Newman)

Adult length 0.9-1.3 inches. Distribution eastern North America from southern Canada to Florida, west to Saskatchewan and New Mexico. *A. abnormis* inhabits creeks and rivers, and occurs with several other large perlids at various localities. Individuals from Gulf Coastal Plains populations are usually darker than those from populations in other regions, but no other differences have been noted. Males have triangular shaped paraprocts and females have a rudimentary subgenital plate. Nymphs are variable but they typically have a well developed M-line on the head and lack anal gills.

Emergence occurs from April through June.

[Clockwise from upper left]

Fig. 5.1. *Acroneuria abnormis* pale form male. TN: Sevier Co., Miegs Creek, 28.v.1993, B. Stark.

Fig. 5.2. *Acroneuria abnormis* dark form male. MS: Simpson Co., Mill Creek, 1.iv.1992, B. Stark.

Fig. 5.3. *Acroneuria abnormis* nymph. NC: Macon Co., Wayah Creek, 10.iii.1992, B. Stark.

Fig. 5.4. *Acroneuria arenosa* male. MS: Simpson Co., Pinola, 3.vi.1993, B. Stark, E. Stark.

Acroneuria arenosa (Pictet)

Adult length 1.0-1.3 inches. Distribution eastern North America along the Atlantic and Gulf Coastal Plains from Pennsylvania to Texas. *A. arenosa* is a species of small to medium sized creeks. In much of the southeast, it occurs with *A. abnormis*. Males have cylindrical paraprocts which are notched on the apical margin, and females have a distinctive, truncate subgenital plate.

Emergence occurs from May through June.

Fig. 5.5. *Acroneuria carolinensis* female. VA: Grayson Co., Fox Creek, 25.v.1990, B. Stark, J. Parham, D. Tanner.

Acroneuria carolinensis (Banks)

Adult length 1.0-1.3 inches. Distribution eastern North America from Quebec to South Carolina. *A. carolinensis* is primarily a species of small rivers and commonly occurs with *A. abnormis*. The species is typically darker than other *Acroneuria*, but pale brown specimens are common among southeastern populations. Females have a distinctive, triangular notch in the subgenital plate margin, and males have short paraprocts which are broad basally, but cylindrical apically. Nymphs usually lack anal gills and have a distinctively banded abdomen.

Emergence occurs from May through July.

Acroneuria evoluta Klapalek

Adult length 0.9-1.3 inches. Distribution midwestern and southern United States from Illinois and Indiana to Florida and Texas. *A. evoluta* is primarily a riverine species. The species was formerly called *A. mela* Frison, and the species formerly known as *A. evoluta* has recently been renamed *A. frisoni*. Males have slender, apically pointed paraprocts, and females have a variable subgenital plate which is typically notched on the lateral margins.

Emergence occurs from May through July.

Fig. 5.6. *Acroneuria evoluta* female. MS: Covington Co., Okatoma River, 4.vi.1993, B. Stark.

Fig. 5.7. *Acroneuria internata* female. WI: Menominee Co., Wolf River, 8.vi.1991, S. Szczytko, J.Dimick, J. Sandberg.

Acroneuria internata (Walker)

Adult length 1.0-1.3 inches. Distribution midwestern and northern United States from Wisconsin and Minnesota to Georgia and Oklahoma. *A. internata* is typically a large river species which occurs with *A. evoluta* and *A. abnormis* in the south and *A. lycorias* in the north. Females have a distinctive bilobed subgenital plate with the lobes directed away from the body, and males have slender, finger-like paraprocts. Males are more easily recognized by shape of the internal genitalia.

Emergence occurs in June and July.

Fig. 5.8. *Acroneuria internata* nymph. WI: Menominee Co., Wolf River, 8.vi.1991, S. Szczytko, J. Dimick, J. Sandberg.

Acroneuria lycorias (Newman)

Adult length 0.8-1.3 inches. Distribution southern Canada from Quebec to Saskatchewan south to Kentucky and Virginia. *A. lycorias* males are very similar to *A. carolinensis* in paraproct structure, and can usually be separated only by examination of internal genitalia. Females are also similar to *A. carolinensis* in subgenital plate shape, but typically the posterior margin is not notched. Nymphs have a well developed M-line on the head, transverse pigment bands on the abdomen, and anal gills are usually present.

Emergence occurs from May to July.

Fig. 5.9. *Acroneuria lycorias* male. WI: Sauk Co., Otter Creek, 24.vi.1991, S. Szczytko, J. Sandberg.

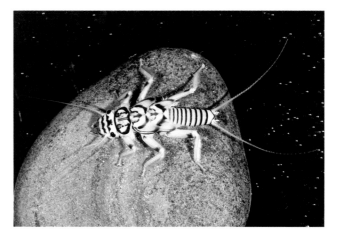

Fig. 5.10. *Acroneuria lycorias* nymph. WI: Sauk Co., Otter Creek, 24.vi.1991, S. Szczytko, J. Sandberg.

Genus *Agnetina*

Three species of these medium to large dark stones, previously known as *Phasganophora* or *Neophasganophora*, occur in eastern North America. Males lack a hammer but have exceptionally long hemitergal processes on segment X, and the Vth abdominal segment bears a prominent dorsal lobe. Females have a small subgenital plate, and adults of both sexes have transverse pigment bands on the meso- and metasterna. Nymphs are distinctively patterned with bright yellow and brown pigment bands, and have a row of peg sensilla behind the ocelli.

Agnetina annulipes (Hagen)

Adult length 0.7-1.2 inches. Distribution Atlantic and Gulf Coastal Plains from Pennsylvania to Louisiana. *A. annulipes* is common in small to medium sized rivers and large creeks. Adults of the species are easily recognized by the dark transverse pigment bands on the base of the mid and hind femora, and males are also distinguished by the long, slender, toe-like apex of the hemitergal processes. The last abdominal segment of nymphs is usually dark apically, and the pale transverse stripe on the head is distinctly M-shaped.

Emergence occurs in May and June.

Fig. 5.11. *Agnetina annulipes* female. MS: Covington Co., Okatoma River, 4.vi.1993, B. Stark.

Fig. 5.12. *Agnetina annulipes* nymph. AL: Tuscaloosa Co., Big Sandy Creek, 26.iii.1993, B. Stark, M. Hicks, C. Haynes.

Agnetina capitata (Pictet)

Adult length 0.8-1.3 inches. Distribution northeastern and midwestern regions from Quebec to Virginia and west to Arkansas. The adult femora have a dark border on the dorsal and ventral margins which surrounds a yellow "window", and the male hemitergal processes are sinuate in lateral aspect. The pale stripe on the nymphal head is not distinctly M-shaped, and the abdominal apex is usually pale.

Emergence occurs in June and July.

Fig. 5.13. *Agnetina capitata* female. VA: Smyth Co., North Fork Holston River, 20.v.1993, B. Kondratieff, F. Kirchner.

Fig. 5.14. *Agnetina capitata* nymph. WI: Shawano Co., Wolf River, 6.vi.1991, S. Szczytko, J. Dimick, J. Sandberg.

Agnetina flavescens (Walsh)

Adult length 0.8-1.2 inches. Distribution midwestern and eastern United States from New York to South Carolina and Oklahoma. The adult femora are dark dorsally and pale on the ventral margins; male hemitergal processes have a short, foot-like apex with a short "toe". The pale pigment band on the nymphal head is almost interrupted by dark pigment, and the abdominal apex is typically pale. Emergence occurs from May to July.

Fig. 5.15. *Agnetina flavescens* female. WI: Shawano Co., Wolf River, 6.vi.1991, S. Szczytko, J. Dimick, J. Sandberg.

Fig. 5.16. *Agnetina flavescens* nymph. WI: Shawano Co., Wolf River, 6.vi.1991, S. Szczytko, J. Dimick, J. Sandberg.

Genus *Anacroneuria*

Anacroneuria is the dominant stonefly genus throughout much of Mexico, Central and South America, but the genus is known from two uncommon species in the southwestern United States, *A. comanche* Stark & Baumann and *A. wipukupa* Baumann & Olson. Adults and nymphs have only two ocelli and they are easily distinguished from biocellate *Neoperla* and *Perlinella* by genitalic features. Males of the *Anacroneuria* species known from the United States have elevated thimble-like hammers, and the females have very large subgenital plates. No photographs are available for this group.

Genus *Attaneuria*

Only one species of this genus, *A. ruralis*, is currently known. Adults resemble those of *Acroneuria* in general appearance, but the eggs, internal genitalia and nymph are quite different from typical *Acroneuria*. Males have a well developed oval hammer on segment IX and the paraprocts are triangular. Females are distinctive due to the small transverse knob on segment VIII, near the subgenital plate base, and nymphs bear an irregular row of short peg sensilla behind the ocelli.

Attaneuria ruralis (Hagen)

Adult length 1.0-1.3 inches. Distribution eastern North America from Pennsylvania and Minnesota to Florida and Arkansas. *A. ruralis* males superficially resemble those of *A. abnormis* but abdominal segments IX and X of *A. ruralis* lack the patches of peg sensilla which occur on *A. abnormis* and the internal genitalia of *A. ruralis* does not have patches of red-brown setae. Females have a poorly developed subgenital plate which bears a small basal knob. Nymphs are brown, with no distinctive pattern, lack anal gills, and have an irregular row of peg sensilla behind the ocelli.

Emergence occurs in June and July.

Fig. 5.17. *Attaneuria ruralis* male. MS: Covington Co., Okatoma River, 4.vi.1993, B. Stark.

Genus *Beloneuria*

This small genus includes three species of pale stones which occur in spring seeps in the southern Appalachians. *B. georgiana* occurs in mid to high elevation streams of Georgia and North Carolina, *B. stewarti* is primarily a Piedmont species, and *B. jamesae* is known from the Cheaha Mountain area of Alabama. Males have short, triangular paraprocts, and a triangular hammer on abdominal segment IX. Females have a long, shallowly notched and triangular subgenital plate while nymphs have an unpatterned abdomen, anal gills, and an inconspicuous M-line on the head. This group was formerly included in *Acroneuria* but the eggs, internal genitalia, and other characters clearly separate these species from that genus.

Beloneuria georgiana (Banks)

Adult length 0.7-1.0 inches. Distribution southern Appalachians of Georgia and North Carolina. *B. georgiana* occurs in small spring seeps of the Blue Ridge Province. Males cannot be easily distinguished from those of other *Beloneuria*, but gravid females are readily distinguished by the golf ball-like appearance of the eggs. Nymphs of *B. georgiana* are currently inseparable from those of *B. stewarti* and *B. jamesae*.

Emergence occurs in May and June.

Fig. 5.18. *Beloneuria georgiana* female. NC: Macon Co., Robin Branch, 21.v.1990, B. Stark, J. Parham, and D. Tanner.

Fig. 5.19. *Beloneuria georgiana* nymph. NC: Macon Co., Robin Branch, 25.v.1993, B. Stark, R. Simmons, and D. Kelly.

Genus *Calineuria*

Only one North American representative, *C. californica* is currently recognized for this group. Adults superficially resemble those of *Acroneuria* but the males have a long, rectangular hammer which readily separates these groups, and the eggs have a well developed collar. Nymphs lack anal gills, but have an irregular row of peg sensilla behind the ocelli.

Calineuria californica (Banks)

Adult length 0.8-1.2 inches. Distribution Pacific coastal area and northern Rocky Mountains from California to British Columbia and Montana. Males have slender, finger-like paraprocts, and the internal genitalia is armed with conspicuous patches of red-brown setae. Females have an unproduced subgenital plate. Males of Owl Creek, Montana populations of this species were reported by Poulton and Stewart (1988) to undergo late afternoon flights to streams where they were observed to splash down in pools. This behavior occurred primarily between 4 and 6 P.M. in late June while female oviposition activity peaked 1-3 hours later at the same site.
Emergence occurs in June and July.

Fig. 5.20. *Calineuria californica* female. CA: El Dorado Co., North Cosumnes River, 21.vi.1995, R. Bottorff.

Fig. 5.21. *Claassenia sabulosa* male. MT: Park Co., Yellowstone River, 21.vii.1989, B. Stark.

Genus *Claassenia*

North America has a single representative of these large golden stones, *C. sabulosa*. Males are short winged, have simple, finger-like hemitergal processes on segment X, and an oval hammer on segment IX. Females are fully winged and the subgenital plate is unproduced. The predaceous nymphs are brightly patterned, have anal gills, and a regularly spaced row of peg sensilla is present behind the ocelli. These insects are an important component of trout stream ecosystems throughout the Rocky Mountains.

Claassenia sabulosa (Banks)

Adult length 1.0-1.3 inches. Distribution northern and western North America from British Columbia to Hudson Bay in Canada, south in the Rockies to Arizona, and in the Cascades and Coastal Ranges, to northern California. This is a species of large rivers such as the Colorado, Gunnison and

Yellowstone. Males usually hide under streamside rocks, driftwood or in crevices of logs by day, but they actively search for females at night. Individuals flushed from hiding places often run swiftly across the water surface.

Emergence occurs from June to August.

Genus *Doroneuria*

Two species of this group, *D. baumanni* and *D. theodora* occur in western North America. *D. theodora* is a species of the northern Rocky Mountains and *D. baumanni* occurs in small streams of the Cascades, Sierra Nevada and Coastal Ranges. Males have slender paraprocts and a prominent, rectangular hammer is present on the IXth abdominal segment. The female subgenital plate is unproduced, and the eggs have a small button-like collar. Long and short winged forms occur for both sexes. Nymphs are often confused with those of *Calineuria* due to their similar color pattern, but *Calineuria* nymphs have a complete fringe of setae on the posterior margin of abdominal segment VII while *Doroneuria* nymphs have a mesal gap in this fringe.

Doroneuria baumanni Stark and Gaufin

Adult length 0.8-1.3 inches. Distribution Coast, Cascade and Sierra Nevada Mountains from British Columbia to California and Nevada. *D. baumanni* can only be distinguished from *D. theodora* by comparing the internal male genitalia, but the two species are not known to overlap in range. The head and thorax of both species is relatively dark.

Emergence occurs from June to September.

Fig. 5.22. *Doroneuria baumanni* female. OR: Tillamook Co., Neskowin Creek, 4.vi.1991, B. Stark, R. Baumann, C. Henderson.

Genus *Eccoptura*

Only one species of this genus, *E. xanthenes*, is currently known. In older literature, *E. xanthenes* was placed in *Acroneuria* but it is now considered distinct. Males have a small, elevated, oval hammer on segment IX and a prominent linear patch of peg sensilla on the dorsum of segment X. Females have a large quadrate notch in the subgenital plate which, together with the pale coloration, makes this one of our most distinctive golden stones. Nymphs have anal gills and are also distinctively patterned with a large area of yellow pigment forward of the median ocellus.

Eccoptura xanthenes (Newman)

Adult length 0.8-1.2 inches. Distribution eastern North America from Connecticut and Ohio to Florida and Mississippi. *E. xanthenes* is a species of small 1st and 2nd order streams in the southeast. Emergence occurs from May through June.

Fig. 5.23. *Eccoptura xanthenes* female. MS: Simpson Co., Mill Creek, 2.v.1992, B. Stark.

Fig. 5.24. *Eccoptura xanthenes* nymph. MS: Simpson Co., Mill Creek, 25.iii.1993, B. Stark.

Genus *Hansonoperla*

This genus was first recognized in 1979 after the discovery of *H. appalachia* in Great Smoky Mountains National Park by C. H. Nelson. However, B. C. Kondratieff and R. F. Kirchner have recently described two additional species of *Hansonoperla* in the eastern United States. Adults and nymphs resemble *Perlinella* but the males have a triangular rather than oval hammer, and the nymphs lack ventral setal fringes on the femora and tibiae.

Hansonoperla appalachia Nelson

Adult length 0.6-0.8 inches. Distribution eastern North America from Massachusetts to Alabama. Adults of this species have three ocelli and are relatively darkly pigmented. The narrow head and anterior eye position of this species also occurs among *Perlinella* species, but they are readily separated by combinations of pigment pattern, ocellar count, or hammer shape.
Emergence occurs in April and May.

Fig. 5.25. *Hansonoperla appalachia* female. TN: Cocke Co., Crying Creek, 28.v.1993, B. Stark.

Genus *Hesperoperla*

This genus includes two species of golden stones, *H. hoguei* and *H. pacifica*. The latter species is widely distributed throughout the west, while *H. hoguei* is restricted to northern California. The paraprocts are small and triangular and the ninth segment bears a large quadrangular hammer. Females have a moderately produced subgenital plate and nymphs display anal gills and an irregular row of peg sensilla behind the ocelli.

Hesperoperla hoguei Baumann & Stark

Adult length 0.75-1.2 inches. Distribution northern Sierra Nevada of California. Adults are virtually identical to *H. pacifica* in genitalic features but are distinctive in pigment pattern. Adults have dark pronotal margins around a broad median yellow field and nymphs have a narrow yellow M-line on the head.

Emergence occurs in May and June.

[Clockwise from upper left]

Fig. 5.26. *Hesperoperla hoguei* male. CA: El Dorado Co., Camp Creek, 11.v.1995, R. Bottorff.

Fig. 5.27. *Hesperoperla pacifica* male. MT: Carbon Co., Rock Creek, 22.vii.1989, B. Stark.

Fig. 5.28. *Hesperoperla pacifica* nymph. CO: Jackson Co., Michigan River, 19.v.1991, C. R. Nelson.

Hesperoperla pacifica (Banks)

Adult length 0.8-1.2 inches. Distribution western North America from Alaska to New Mexico and California. *H. pacifica* is a widely distributed species which occurs in rivers, creeks and springs, and both short and long winged forms are known. Among western perlids, males are easily distinguished by the quadrate hammer, females by the produced subgenital plate, and nymphs by a wide longitudinal yellow band extending from the median ocellus to the labrum. *H. hoguei* occurs with *H. pacifica* in some northern California streams.

Emergence occurs from April through September.

Genus *Neoperla*

Fourteen species of these medium golden stones are recognized in eastern North America, with the greatest diversity occuring in the Ozarks and Ouachitas. Males have complex genitalia which includes dorsal lobes on segments VII and VIII, hemitergal lobes with finger-like processes, and long spiny internal organs; hammers are absent. Females usually have a small tab-like subgenital plate, and adults of both sexes have only two ocelli which distinguishes them from most perlids. Nymphs have 2 ocelli, anal gills, and a low ridge extending across the head behind the ocelli.

Neoperla clymene (Newman)

Adult length 0.5-0.8 inches. Distribution eastern North America from Virginia to Florida and Texas. This species can be distinguished from other *Neoperla* by shape of the internal male and female genitalia and by egg chorion structure. Stark and Lentz (1988) present a key based on these characters which permits separation of American *Neoperla* in this species complex.

Emergence occurs in May and June.

Fig. 5.29. *Neoperla clymene* female. MS: Simpson Co., Pinola, 15.vi.1993, S. Curtis.

Fig. 5.30. *Neoperla robisoni* female. MS: Simpson Co., Pinola, 3.vi.1993, B. Stark, E. Stark.

Neoperla robisoni Poulton and Stewart

Adult length 0.5-0.8 inches. Known distribution lower Mississippi Valley from Missouri to Mississippi. This species occurs with *N. clymene* in Mississippi, and with various other *Neoperla* at other localities. Adults have less prominently banded femora than *N. clymene* specimens, but the two species are reliably separated by study of dissected internal genitalia.

Emergence occurs in May and June.

Neoperla stewarti Stark and Baumann

Adult length 0.5-0.8 inches. Known distribution Maine and Wisconsin to Mississippi and Alabama. This species also occurs with *N. clymene* at some Mississippi and Alabama localities. The two species can be distinguished using internal genitalic and egg characters.

Emergence occurs in May and June.

Fig. 5.31. *Neoperla stewarti* nymph. WI: Menominee Co., Wolf River, 6.vi.1991, S. Szczytko, J. Dimick, J. Sandberg.

Genus *Paragnetina*

Five species of these large stones are currently recognized in eastern North America. Males usually have lobes on segment V, short, foot-shaped hemitergal lobes, and hammers are absent. Females have notched subgenital plates, and the eggs have stalked collars. Nymphs are usually brightly patterned, have a straight row of peg sensilla behind the ocelli, and most species lack anal gills.

Paragnetina fumosa (Banks)

Adult length 0.6-1.1 inches. Distribution eastern North America along the Coastal Plains from Pennsylvania to Texas. *P. fumosa* is a dark species. The males have a narrow notch in the lobe on segment V and the hemitergal processes are truncate apically. Females have a triangular subgenital plate with a shallow quadrate notch. Nymphs are brightly patterned and occur in leaf packs of small southeastern streams with *Acroneuria arenosa* and *A. abnormis*.

Emergence occurs from April through June.

Fig. 5.32. *Paragnetina fumosa* female. MS: Simpson Co., Mill Creek, 15.iv.1992, B. Stark.

Fig. 5.33. *Paragnetina fumosa* nymph. MS: Simpson Co., Bush Creek, 3.iv.1993, B. Stark.

Paragnetina immarginata (Say)

Adult length 0.8-1.3 inches. Distribution eastern North America from Quebec to northern Georgia and South Carolina. Adult males are similar to *P. fumosa* in having the lobe on segment V notched, but the hemitergal processes are upturned apically. Females have a short, wide and shallowly notched subgenital plate, and nymphs are perhaps the most attractively patterned of American stoneflies. This species occurs in creeks and rivers of the Appalachians.

Emergence occurs from July to September.

Fig. 5.34. *Paragnetina immarginata* nymph. NC: Macon Co., Tellico Creek, 27.v.1993, B. Stark, R. Simmons, D. Kelly.

Fig. 5.35. *Paragnetina kansensis* female. MS: Covington Co., Okatoma River, 4.iv.1993, B. Stark.

Paragnetina kansensis (Banks)

Adult length 0.7-1.2 inches. Distribution midwestern and southern United States from Kansas and Indiana to Louisiana and Florida. *P. kansensis* is a pale yellow species found in larger creeks and rivers. Males have no lobe on segment V, and females have a triangular subgenital plate with a small quadrate notch. Nymphs resembles those of *P. media* but anal gills are usually present in female nymphs.

Emergence occurs in June and July.

Paragnetina media (Walker)

Adult length 0.6-1.1 inches. Distribution southern Canada from Saskatchewan and Quebec to Arkansas and Virginia. Males have a broad, rounded lobe on segment V, and females have a small triangular subgenital plate with a rounded notch. Nymphs are brown with an obscure pattern. This species is quite similar to *P. ichusa* from the southern Appalachians.

Emergence occurs from May to July.

Fig. 5.36. *Paragnetina media* female. WI: Portage Co., Tomorrow River, 18.v.1991, S. Szczytko.

Fig. 5.37. *Paragnetina media* nymph. WI: Portage Co., Tomorrow River, 8.vi.1990, S. Szczytko.

Fig. 5.38. *Perlesta cinctipes* male. OK: Latimer Co., Rock Creek, 18.v.1992, B. Stark.

Genus *Perlesta*

Fourteen species of these small stones are currently recognized in North America. Males lack a hammer and dorsal lobes, but the paraprocts are developed into erect terminal hooks which often bear an apical spine. Females have a slightly produced and often broadly bilobed subgenital plate. Nymphs are usually freckled with brown pigment and have anal gills.

Perlesta cinctipes (Banks)

Adult length 0.4-0.6 inches. Distribution Kansas and Iowa to Oklahoma and Arkansas. This is a dark species with banded femora. Males have long slender paraprocts which bear an anterior subapical spine. The female subgenital plate is shallowly notched and the mesal field is weakly sclerotized. Nymphs have a dark band across the ocellar region and the area forward of this is entirely pale. The egg is covered with shallow pits and has a stalked collar.

Emergence occurs in May and June.

Perlesta decipiens (Walsh)

Adult length 0.5-0.7 inches. Distribution midwestern and western North America from Wisconsin and Virginia to Wyoming and Texas. Males of this yellow-brown species have apically rounded paraprocts with a small subapical spine. The female subgenital plate lobes are usually truncate and the smooth or slightly pitted egg has a short, wide collar. Nymphs are similar to those of *P. cinctipes* but the pronotal margins are usually paler than the dark band on the head.

Emergence occurs from May to August.

Fig. 5.39. *Perlesta decipiens* female. VA: Scott Co., Clinch River, 23.v.1993, B. Kondratieff, F. Kirchner.

47

Fig. 5.40. *Perlesta decipiens* nymph. WI: Menominee Co., Wolf River, 6.vi.1991, S. Szczytko, J. Dimick, J. Sandberg.

Fig. 5.41. *Perlesta decipiens* mating pair. TX: Blanco Co., Pedernales River, 24.iv.1992, C. R. Nelson.

Perlesta placida (Hagen)

Adult length 0.5-0.6 inches. Distribution Coastal Plains of eastern North America from Maine to Louisiana. *P. placida* is a dark brown species with contrasting pale costal wing margins. The male paraprocts are broadly triangular and bear a minute apical tooth. The female subgenital plate is shallowly notched and the egg is pitted and has a short broad collar. The nymph is undescribed.

Emergence occurs in May and June.

Fig. 5.42. *Perlesta placida* male. MS: Simpson Co., Pinola, 3.vi.1993, B. Stark, E. Stark.

Fig. 5.43. *Perlesta shubuta* female. MS: Simpson Co., Pinola, 3.vi.1993, B. Stark, E. Stark.

Perlesta shubuta Stark

Adult length 0.3-0.5 inches. Known distribution lower Mississippi Valley from Missouri to Mississippi. The dark brown males have short paraprocts with slanted tips, and the female subgenital plate lobes are truncate. The smooth egg bears a narrow stalked collar, and the nymph has conspicuous brown spots scattered over the head and abdomen.

Emergence occurs in May and June.

Genus *Perlinella*

Three species of slender bodied dark stones are included in this genus. Males bear oval hammers on segment IX and have slender curved paraprocts. Females have slightly produced and broadly notched subgenital plates and the nymphal legs bear dorsal and ventral fringes of long setae. There are usually two rows of crossveins in the forewing anal area.

Perlinella drymo (Newman)

Adult length 0.5-0.9 inches. Distribution eastern North America from Maine and Minnesota to Florida and Texas. Adults have three ocelli and a longitudinally banded pronotum with a narrow median stripe. Male internal genitalia include a pair of sclerites with serrate lateral margins. Nymphs are brown with darker patterns on the head and thorax, and slender anal gills are present.

Emergence occurs from February to April.

Fig. 5.44. *Perlinella drymo* female. MS: Claiborne Co., Kennison Creek, 28.ii.1992, B. Stark.

Fig. 5.45. *Perlinella drymo* nymph. MS: Claiborne Co., Ragsdale Creek, 7.ii.1993, B. Stark.

Perlinella ephyre (Newman)

Adult length 0.4-0.6 inches. Distribution eastern North America from New York and Minnesota to Florida and Oklahoma. Adults of this species have two ocelli and the pronotum usually has pale areas on the disc. The sclerites of the male internal genitalia have sharply curved apical processes on the inner margins, and the nymphs are pale brown with inconspicuous anal gills.

Emergence occurs in April and May.

Fig. 5.46. *Perlinella ephyre* male. VA: Scott Co., Clinch River, 23.v.1993, B. Kondratieff, F. Kirchner.

Perlinella zwicki Kondratieff, Kirchner and Stewart

Adult length 0.4-0.6 inches. Distribution southeastern United States from South Carolina to Mississippi. Adults of this species have two ocelli and a dark pronotum. Sclerites of the internal male genitalia are laterally serrate and lack sharply curved apical processes. Nymphs are similar to those of *P. ephyre* but are typically darker.

Emergence occurs in May and June.

Fig. 5.47. *Perlinella zwicki* male. MS: Simpson Co., Mill Creek, 8.vi.1993, B. Stark, W. Cavett.

CHAPTER 6

FAMILY PERLODIDAE—THE STRIPETAILS & SPRINGFLIES

Perlodids are medium to large stoneflies comprising two distinctive subfamilies, Isoperlinae (stripetails) and Perlodinae (springflies). Nymphs of many genera lack gills but some possess simple, finger-like gills on the submentum, neck or thorax and *Oroperla* nymphs also display lateral gills on abdominal segments I-VII. Isoperline males have sclerotized paraprocts, an entire Xth tergum and the epiproct is undeveloped, but the perlodine genera usually have a cleft Xth tergum, well developed epiproct and the paraprocts are typically membranous. *Diura* is an exceptional perlodine with entire tergum X, sclerotized paraprocts and no epiproct. Egg shape varies from modified turtle or 3-sided eggs to those with a typical oval shape; *Isoperla* eggs are oval but usually have an asymmetrical indentation. Around trout streams these insects are sometimes referred to as "medium browns", "willow flies", "yellow stones" or "yellow sallies" and several nymph and adult patterns with these names are modeled after species of *Isogenoides* and *Isoperla*. Thirty genera and 122 species of perlodids are currently recognized for North America.

Genus *Arcynopteryx*

This genus is represented in North America by *A. compacta* (McLachlan). This species ranges from Alaska to Maine and has been reported as far south as Colorado. Males usually have shortened wings and are easily recognized by the long, lash-like epiproct tip. Females and nymphs are quite similar to *Skwala*. *A. compacta* has been collected around alpine lakes in the northern Rocky Mountains. No photographs are available for this group.

Genus *Baumannella*

This genus is represented by a single uncommon California species, *B. alameda* (Needham & Claassen). Adults are similar to *Kogotus* but males lack peg sensilla on abdominal segment IX and the biconcave egg is unlike that of any other member of the family. No photographs are available for this group.

Genus *Calliperla*

Only one species, *C. luctuosa*, an inhabitant of spring seeps in the Coast and Cascade Mountains, is known. Nymphs are gill-less and resemble robust *Isoperla*. Males have a membranous, projecting epiproct, but the Xth tergum is entire. A small lobe is present on sternum VIII.

Calliperla luctuosa (Banks)

Adult length 0.6-0.8 inches. Distribution western North America from Washington to California. Adults are usually swept from vegetation around springs and 1st order streams, often only a few meters from a large stream.
Emergence typically occurs from May through July.

Fig. 6.1. *Calliperla luctuosa* male and female. OR: Curry Co., seeps in Elk River Canyon, 2.vi.1991, B. Stark, R. Baumann, C. Henderson.

Genus *Cascadoperla*

This genus is represented by a single uncommon species in the Pacific Northwest. *Cascadoperla* is an *Isoperla*-like genus but males have a pair of upturned apical processes on the Xth tergum and no lobe occurs on sternum VIII. No photographs are available for this group.

Genus *Chernokrilus*

This small genus includes two uncommon species known from California and Oregon. Nymphs and adults are usually collected from springs and small headwater streams of the Coast and Cascade Mountains. Males have lobes on sterna VII or VIII, a well developed epiproct, rounded lateral stylets and the Xth tergum is cleft.

Chernokrilus misnomus (Claassen)

Adult length 0.6-0.8 inches. Distribution Oregon and California. Nymphs resemble those of *Calliperla* but lack the pale abdominal stripe. Adults are black with bright yellow head and pronotal patterns. Emergence occurs from May through July.

Fig. 6.2. *Chernokrilus misnomus* male. OR: Benton Co., Yew Creek, 4.vi.1991, B. Stark, R. Baumann, C. Henderson.

Fig. 6.3. *Clioperla clio* female. WI: Sauk Co., Otter Creek, 24.vi.1991, S. Szczytko, J. Sandberg.

Genus *Clioperla*

This genus includes only the single, widespread eastern species, *C. clio*. Nymphs lack gills and have a yellow-brown body color and distinctive dark head pattern. Males are recognized by the shallow apical notch on tergum X.

Clioperla clio (Newman)

Adult length 0.6-0.8 inches. Distribution eastern North America from Ontario to Oklahoma and Florida; common in streams throughout the Ouachitas and in the Gulf Coastal Plains and Piedmont regions of the southeast. In addition to the notched tergum X, males have a basal lobe on sternum VIII. Emergence occurs from February to April.

Fig. 6.4. *Clioperla clio* nymph. WI: Sauk Co., Otter Creek, 24.vi.1991, S. Szczytko, J. Sandberg.

Genus *Cosumnoperla*

Cosumnoperla includes the uncommon species, *C. hypocrena*, presently known only from headwater streams of the Cosumnes River drainage in California. Adults and nymphs resemble robust *Isoperla* specimens but males have an unusual notched and triangular shaped process on tergum X.

Cosumnoperla hypocrena Szczytko & Bottorff

Adult length 0.6-0.75 inches. Distribution northern Sierra Nevada Mountains of California. Adults have a median pale pronotal spot, the female subgenital plate is deeply notched and the male Xth tergal process is unique.

Emergence occurs in May and June.

Fig. 6.5. *Cosumnoperla hypocrena* female [left]. CA: El Dorado Co., intermittent stream, 11.v.1995, R. Bottorff.

Fig. 6.6. *Cultus aestivalis* male [right]. CO: Larimer Co., Cache la Poudre River, 7.vii.1995, B. Kondratieff.

Genus *Cultus*

This small genus of five species is represented in the Appalachians and surrounding area by *C. decisus* (*C. decisus decisus, C. decisus isolatus*) and *C. verticalis* and in the western mountains by *C. aestivalis*, *C. pilatus* and *C. tostonus*. Nymphs lack gills and have few setae on the head and pronotum. Males have a cleft tergum X, moderately developed but simple epiproct and long sclerotized lateral stylets. Eggs are turtle shaped.

Cultus aestivalis (Needham & Claassen)

Adult length 0.4-0.6 inches. Distribution western North America from Yukon and Northwest Territory to Arizona and New Mexico. Males have a large lobe on sternum VII, a small lobe on sternum VIII and a poorly developed anterior epiproct sclerite. This species is distinguished from other western species primarily by shape of the lateral stylets in the male.

Emergence occurs from April through August.

Cultus verticalis (Banks)

Adult length 0.5-0.6 inches. Distribution eastern North America from Quebec to North Carolina and Tennessee. Males have a large lobe on sternum VII, a small lobe on sternum VIII and minute teeth along the anterior epiproct sclerite.

Emergence occurs in April and May.

Fig. 6.7. *Cultus verticalis* female. NC: Macon Co., Cullasaja River, 26.v.1993, B. Stark, R. Simmons, D. Kelly.

Fig. 6.8. *Diploperla morgani* female. VA: Smyth Co., North Fork Holston River, 20.v.1993, B. Kondratieff, F. Kirchner.

Genus *Diploperla*

This small group of eastern springflies is closely related to *Cultus*. Four species are currently recognized and they are most common in the Appalachians. Males are usually recognized by a poorly developed epiproct, well developed lateral stylets and lobes on sterna VII and VIII. Tergum X is cleft in males and the eggs are turtle shaped.

Diploperla morgani Kondratieff & Voshell

Adult length 0.5-0.7 inches. Distribution North Carolina and Virginia. Males have prominent, apically forked lateral stylets.

Emergence is recorded in May.

Diploperla robusta Stark & Gaufin

Adult length 0.5-0.7 inches. Distribution eastern North America from Connecticut and Indiana to Kentucky and Virginia. Apices of the male lateral stylets are rounded to acute and scythe-shaped in lateral aspect.

Emergence is recorded in April and May.

Fig. 6.9. *Diploperla robusta* male. OH: Lawrence Co., Storms Creek, 19.v.1993, B. Kondratieff, F. Kirchner.

Genus *Diura*

Three species of *Diura* are recorded in North America but *D. bicaudata* and *D. nanseni*, two primarily European species, are uncommon and known only from isolated northern localities. *D. knowltoni*, however, is relatively common in the west. Males have the Xth tergum entire and the paraprocts modified into a pair of thick posteriorly-directed lobes. Eggs are triangular in cross section.

Diura knowltoni (Frison)

Adult length 0.7-0.9 inches. Distribution western North America from Yukon to California and New Mexico. The brightly colored nymphs of this species are usually found in moderate size streams and at intermediate elevations in the mountains.
Emergence occurs from April through June.

Fig. 6.10. *Diura knowltoni* nymph. CO: Larimer Co., Michigan River, 18.v.1991, S. Szczytko, B. Stark.

Fig. 6.11. *Diura knowltoni* female. CO: Routt Co., Bear River, 27.v.1995, B. Stark, J. Parham, C. Massey.

Genus *Frisonia*

Frisonia is represented by a single uncommon species of the Sierras and Cascades, *F. picticeps*. Males have the Xth tergum cleft and a slender, somewhat cylindrical epiproct flanked by prominent lateral stylets. Submental gills are present on adults and nymphs but other gills are absent.

Frisonia picticeps (Hanson)

Adult length 0.7-0.9 inches. Distribution western North America from British Columbia along the mountains to California and Nevada. Males are typically short winged while females are fully winged and have several irregular apical crossveins. The male hemitergal lobes are long, slender and curved upward near the apex.
Emergence occurs from May through July.

Fig. 6.12. *Frisonia picticeps* male. CA: El Dorado Co., Truckee River, 13.vii.1995, R. Bottorff, K. Alexander..

Genus *Helopicus*

Helopicus includes three species of eastern springflies whose nymphs typically bear a single bold transverse head band. Submental gills are well developed in adults and nymphs and males have the Xth tergum cleft. The epiproct is prominent but lateral stylets are absent. The egg is triangular in cross section.

Helopicus bogaloosa Stark & Ray

Adult length 0.6-0.8 inches. Distribution Costal Plains from North Carolina to the Mississippi River. Newly emerged adults of this black species have areas of red pigmentation in the soft tissues around the thorax. Males have a flat dorsal surface of the epiproct.
Emergence is recorded in February and March.

Fig. 6.13. *Helopicus bogaloosa* male. MS: Simpson Co., Rials Creek, 4.ii.1995, B. Stark..

Fig. 6.14. *Helopicus subvarians* female. NC: Macon Co., Cullasaja River, 24.v.1993, B. Kondratieff, F. Kirchner..

Helopicus subvarians (Banks)

Adult length 0.6-0.8 inches. Distribution eastern North America from Ontario and Quebec to Alabama and Florida. Adults of this species are dark but the wings are translucent. The dorsal surface of the male epiproct bears a pair of longitudinal ridges adjacent to the central sclerite.
Emergence begins in March in the southeast and continues through June in the north.

Genus *Hydroperla*

Four species of eastern and midwestern springflies are currently included in *Hydroperla*, but only *H. crosbyi* is commonly collected. Adults are similar to *Helopicus* but male *Hydroperla, except H. rickeri*, have lateral stylets. Submental gills are well developed and the eggs are triangular in cross section.

Hydroperla crosbyi (Needham & Claassen)

Adult length 0.8-1.1 inches. Distribution midwestern North America from Illinois and Indiana to Texas. The anterior face of the epiproct is cup-like and the posterior aspect bears a slender decurved hook.
Emergence occurs from February through April.

Fig. 6.15. *Hydroperla crosbyi* nymph. TX: Travis Co., Bull Creek, 23.ii.1991, C. R. Nelson.

Fig. 6.16. *Hydroperla crosbyi* female. TX: Gillespie Co., Pedernales River, 13.iii.1993, C. R. Nelson.

Hydroperla fugitans (Needham & Claassen)

Adult length 0.7-0.9 inches. Distribution midwestern North America from Illinois and Indiana to Texas. The epiproct of this species lacks the decurved hook on the posterior face but bears a prominent anterior hook. This is an infrequently collected species of large rivers.

Emergence occurs in March and April.

Fig. 6.17. *Hydroperla fugitans* male. MO: Boon Co., Missouri River, 25.ii.1995, B. Poulton.

Genus *Isogenoides*

Isogenoides currently includes nine species distributed primarily in the north and mountainous regions of the east and west, but they may also occur in lowland coldwater streams. Both adults and nymphs are distinguished from other genera of springflies by the presence of a median groove on the mesosternum. Submental gills are long, the egg is triangular in cross section and the male Xth tergum is cleft. Lateral stylets are present but the epiproct is somewhat variable.

Isogenoides olivaceus (Walker)

Adult length 0.6-0.8 inches. Distribution Great Lakes region from Quebec to Minnesota. The male epiproct bears a distinctive lash-like process in this species.

Emergence occurs from April through June.

Fig. 6.19. *Isogenoides olivaceus* nymph. WI: Oconto Co., South Branch Oconto River, 27.iv.1991, S. Szczytko, J. Dimick, J. Sandberg.

Fig. 6.18. *Isogenoides olivaceus* male. WI: Florence Co., Woods Creek, 28.iv.1991, S. Szczytko, J. Dimick, J. Sandberg.

Genus *Isoperla*

This large genus of "medium yellow" or "stripetail" stoneflies includes 57 currently recognized species. Males have a lobe on sternum VIII, paraprocts are hardened and modified as hooks and the Xth tergum is uncleft. In many species the nymphs have three longitudinal stripes on the abdomen and adults and nymphs do not have gills. In the western states, the "mormon girl" is a well known fly patterned after *I. mormona* and the "yellow sally" patterns are modeled, at least in part, for *I. bilineata* in the east and *I. quinquepunctata* in the west. Szczytko & Stewart (1979) reviewed the western species of *Isoperla* and Szczytko is currently working on the eastern complex.

Isoperla bilineata (Say)

Adult length 0.4-0.6 inches. Distribution Atlantic Canada and Saskatchewan to Mississippi and North Carolina. Adults are yellow and typically have the ocelli connected with a dark V-shaped mark. The nymphal head region is dark but a small yellow spot occurs between the posterior ocelli.

Emergence occurs from April to July.

Fig. 6.20. *Isoperla bilineata* nymph. WI: Eau Claire Co., Chippewa River, 12.vi.1992, J. Cahow.

[Clockwise from upper left]

Fig. 6.21. *Isoperla bilineata* female. WI: Eau Claire Co., Chippewa River, 12.vi.1992, J. Cahow.

Fig. 6.22. *Isoperla cotta* nymph. WI: Bayfield Co., Sioux River, J. Cahow.

Fig. 6.23. *Isoperla cotta* female. WI: Lincoln Co., Ripley Creek, 8.vi.1991, J. Sandberg.

Isoperla cotta Ricker

Adult length 0.4-0.6 inches. Distribution Atlantic Canada and Minnesota to the Carolinas. Adults of this species are darker than *I. bilineata* and fresh adults have an olive green cast. Most of the ocellar area is covered by a dark quadrangle which often includes a pale spot. Nymphs are yellow with narrow brown abdominal stripes and a distinctive head pattern. This species is found in high quality trout streams and is uncommon throughout its range.
Emergence occurs from May through July.

Isoperla dicala Frison

Adult length 0.4-0.5 inches. Distribution Quebec and Manitoba to Florida and Mississippi. Adults are generally similar to *I. bilineata* but males have a long, narrow lobe on sternum VIII. Nymphs have a dark brown head with a few small pale areas and a distinctively freckled abdomen covered with stout hairs.
Emergence occurs from April through June.

Isoperla distincta Nelson

Adult length 0.35-0.5 inches. Distribution southern Appalachians of Tennessee and the Carolinas. This unusual isoperline has dorsal knobs on segments V, VI and IX and lateral knobs on segment 5 of the male abdomen.
Emergence occurs in April and May.

[Clockwise from upper left]

Fig. 6.24. *Isoperla dicala* nymph. WI: Portage Co., Spring Creek, 18.vi.1991, J. Dimick, J. Sandberg.

Fig. 6.25. *Isoperla dicala* female. WI: Portage Co., Spring Creek, 18.vi.1991, J. Dimick, J. Sandberg.

Fig. 6.26. *Isoperla distincta* male. NC: Macon Co., Arrowwood Glade, 26.v.1994, S. Szczytko, B. Stark, J. Sandberg.

Isoperla frisoni Illies

Adult length 0.4-0.6 inches. Distribution Atlantic Canada and Manitoba to North Carolina. Adults resemble *I. bilineata* and *I. dicala* but nymphs are distinctively striped on the thorax and abdomen and the dark head band is continuous.

Emergence occurs from April through June.

Fig. 6.27. *Isoperla frisoni* nymph. WI: Waushara Co., Bird Creek, 9.v.1991, S. Szczytko, J. Sandberg, J. Cahow.

Fig. 6.28. *Isoperla frisoni* female. WI: Oneida Co., Bearskin Creek, 20.viii.1992, C. R. Nelson.

Isoperla fulva Claassen

Adult length 0.5-0.7 inches. Distribution Alberta and British Columbia to California and New Mexico. This species is ubiquitous in streams throughout the Rocky Mountains.
Emergence occurs from April through August.

[Clockwise from upper left]

Fig. 6.29. *Isoperla fulva* mating pair. NM: Sandoval Co., Jemez River, 29.v.1991, C. R. Nelson.

Fig. 6.30. *Isoperla lata* nymph. WI: Lincoln Co., Ripley Creek, 19.iv.1992, J. Sandberg.

Fig. 6.31. *Isoperla lata* male. WI: Lincoln Co., Ripley Creek, 17.iv.1989, S. Szczytko, J. Sandberg.

Isoperla lata Frison

Adult length 0.5-0.7 inches. Distribution Nova Scotia and Minnesota to Tennessee. Adults are dark brown with a narrow yellow pronotal stripe and pale areas near the eyes and ocellar triangle. The nymphal abdomen bears a narrow median and broad lateral stripes and a distinctive head pattern. This species is found most commonly in cold high quality trout streams.
Emergence occurs from April through May.

Isoperla marlynia (Needham & Claassen)

Adult length 0.4-0.6 inches. Distribution Atlantic Canada and Saskatchewan to Colorado and South Carolina. Adults are brown with yellow markings scattered over the head and nymphs lack the usual "stripetail" appearance but have transverse bands on the abdomen.
Emergence occurs from April through May.

[Clockwise from upper left]

Fig. 6.32. *Isoperla marlynia* nymph. WI: Florence Co., Pine River, 14.iv.1992, S. Szczytko, J. Dimick.

Fig. 6.33. *Isoperla marlynia* male. WI: Florence Co., Pine River, 14.iv.1992, S. Szczytko, J. Dimick.

Fig. 6.34. *Isoperla mormona* male. NM: Lincoln Co., Rio Bonito, 29.v.1995, B. Stark, C. Massey, K. Simpson.

Isoperla mormona Banks

Adult length 0.4-0.6 inches. Distribution Montana and British Columbia to Baja California and New Mexico. Adults of this yellow-brown species typically have red on the abdominal venter and the male vesicle is quadrate.

Emergence occurs from May to August.

Isoperla nana (Walsh)

Adult length 0.25-0.4 inches. This tiny *Isoperla* is distributed from Quebec and Wisconsin to Kentucky. Adults are predominantly black with white margins on the forewings and nymphs are also dark but with a distinctive head pattern.

Emergence occurs in April and May.

Isoperla phalerata (Smith)

Adult length 0.5-0.7 inches. Distribution South Dakota and Oregon to New Mexico. Adults of this dark brown species are recognized by the presence of several crossveins in branches of the R veins. The nymphal head is brown with a pale spot forward of the median ocellus and pale bands behind the lateral ocelli.

Emergence occurs from April through August.

Fig. 6.35. *Isoperla nana* nymph. WI: Green Co., Bell Fountain Creek, 24.iv.1991, S. Szczytko, J. Sandberg.

Fig. 6.36. *Isoperla nana* male. WI: Green Lake Co., Bell Fountain Creek, 24.iv.1991, S. Szczytko, J. Sandberg.

Fig. 6.37. *Isoperla phalerata* nymph. NM: Taos Co., Rio Fernando de Taos, 20.v.1991, B. Stark, S. Szczytko, C. R. Nelson.

Fig. 6.38. *Isoperla phalerata* male. NM: Taos Co., Rio Fernando de Taos, 20.v.1991, B. Stark, S. Szczytko, C. R. Nelson.

Isoperla pinta Frison

Adult length 0.4-0.6 inches. Distribution Alberta and British Columbia to Baja California and Colorado. Adults of this species have a checkered pattern of black and yellow on the pronotum and nymphs are also distinctively patterned on the head and thorax.

Emergence occurs from March through July.

Fig. 6.39. *Isoperla pinta* nymph. CO: Jackson Co., Michigan River, 19.v.1991, C. R. Nelson.

Fig. 6.40. *Isoperla pinta* male. CO: Jackson Co., Michigan River, 17.v.1991, S. Szczytko, B. Stark.

Isoperla quinquepunctata (Banks)

Adult length 0.45-0.6 inches. Distribution British Columbia and Saskatchewan to Baja California and New Mexico. Adults of this common species often have dark red-brown abdominal pigmentation and some populations include both short wing and long wing males.

Emergence occurs from April through August.

[Clockwise from upper left]

Fig. 6.41. *Isoperla quinquepunctata* male. CO: Larimer Co., Cache la Poudre River, 7.vii.1995, B. Kondratieff.

Fig. 6.42. *Isoperla richardsoni* nymph. WI: Shawano Co., Wolf River, 6.vi.1991, S. Szczytko, J. Sandberg, J. Dimick.

Fig. 6.43. *Isoperla richardsoni* male. WI: Shawano Co., Wolf River, 6.vi.1991, S. Szczytko, J. Sandberg, J. Dimick.

Isoperla richardsoni Frison

Adult length 0.4-0.6 inches. Distribution Connecticut and Minnesota to Missouri and West Virginia. Adults are pale and resemble *I. bilineata* but nymphs are conspicuously striped and have a dark head and pronotal pattern.

Emergence occurs in May and June.

Isoperla signata (Banks)

Adult length 0.5-0.75 inches. Distribution Nova Scotia and Minnesota to Oklahoma and Virginia. Adults are dark brown or black patterned with yellow and nymphs lack the usual longitudinal striped pattern on the abdomen but have alternating transverse pigment bands. This is one of the more common *Isoperla* species in the upper midwest.

Emergence occurs in April and May.

Fig. 6.44. *Isoperla signata* nymph. WI: Waushara
Co., Bird Creek, 6.v.1989, S. Szczytko.

Fig. 6.45. *Isoperla signata* male. WI: Waushara
Co., Bird Creek, 6.v.1989, S. Szczytko.

Isoperla slossonae (Banks)

Adult length 0.5-0.7 inches. Distribution Atlantic Canada and Minnesota to North Carolina. Adults of this species are dark brown with a pale ocellar spot and banded femora, and the nymphal abdomen bears a row of paired median spots.

Emergence occurs in April and May.

Fig. 6.46. *Isoperla slossonae* nymph. WI: Portage Co., Tomorrow River, 5.iv.1987, S. Szczytko.

Fig. 6.47. *Isoperla slossonae* male. WI: Portage
Co., Tomorrow River, 5.iv.1987, S. Szczytko.

Isoperla sobria (Hagen)

Adult length 0.5-0.7 inches. Distribution Alaska to California and New Mexico. Adults are dark with several pale areas on the head and the nymphal abdominal segments have eight rows of paired pale spots.

Emergence occurs from May to August.

Isoperla transmarina (Newman)

Adult length 0.5-0.7 inches. Distribution Atlantic Canada and British Columbia to Kentucky and Virginia. This species is transcontinental in the Canadian Provinces but only penetrates south-ward along the Appalachians. Adults are dark brown with a pale ocellar spot.

Emergence occurs in May and June.

Fig. 6.48. *Isoperla sobria* nymph. NM: Taos Co., Rio Fernando de Taos, 20.v.1991, B. Stark, S. Szczytko, C. R. Nelson.

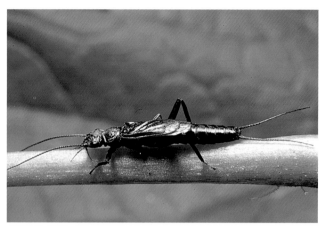

Fig. 6.49. *Isoperla sobria* male. UT: Utah Co., South Fork of American Fork River, 17.vii.1995, C. Nelson.

Fig. 6.50. *Isoperla transmarina* nymph. WI: Shawano Co., Comet Creek, 10.v.1990, S. Szczytko.

Fig. 6.51. *Isoperla transmarina* male. WI: Shawano Co., Comet Creek, 10.v.1990, S. Szczytko.

Genus *Kogotus*

This genus includes two medium-size, dark-bodied perlodines common to the western mountain ranges. Males have a cleft Xth tergum and an unusual epiproct with the apex coiled internally. Nymphs, like those of *Rickera*, bear a single maxillary tooth.

Kogotus modestus (Banks)

Adult length 0.6-0.7 inches. Distribution British Columbia and Montana to New Mexico. Males of this species are traditionally distinguished from those of *K. nonus* by the relative length of the hemitergal lobes.

Emergence occurs from May through August.

Fig. 6.52. *Kogotus modestus* male. CO: Summit Co., Boulder Creek, 3.ix.1995, B. Kondratieff.

67

Genus *Malirekus*

Malirekus includes two large Appalachian perlodines with dark brown or black adult pigmentation. Males have a cleft 10th tergum and a large epiproct clothed with red brown setae. A broad lobe is present on sternum VII and the lateral stylets are hooked apically. Nymphs and adults usually have short submental gills and the eggs are triangular in cross section. *M. iroquois* occurs from Quebec and New Brunswick to Pennsylvania and *M. hastatus* is a southern Appalachian species.

Malirekus hastatus (Banks)

Adult length 0.9-1.1 inches. Distribution Kentucky and Virginia to Georgia and South Carolina. *M. hastatus* is common in small streams throughout the southern Appalachians where it is often the largest carnivorous insect.
Emergence occurs from May through June.

Fig. 6.53. *Malirekus hastatus* male. NC: Jackson Co., Mull Creek, 26.v.1993, B. Stark, R. Simmons, D. Kelly.

Genus *Megarcys*

This is a group of five western Nearctic and a few eastern Palearctic species. The genus is exceptionally distinctive with nymphs and adults displaying single finger-like gills on each thoracic segment and on the submentum. Males have a cleft 10th tergum and large epiproct with a conical, "windsock-like" posterior process. Lateral stylets are well developed and the egg is basically circular in cross section but with scalloped margins. *Megarcys* is often common in creeks and small rivers of the Cascades and Rocky Mountains.

Megarcys signata (Hagen)

Adult length 0.7-1.0 inches. Distribution Alaska to New Mexico. Males are similar to *M. watertoni* but are usually separated on the basis of a more extensive patch of sensilla in the median field of tergum IX in *M. signata*.

Megarcys watertoni (Ricker)

Adult length 0.7-1.0 inches. Distribution northern Rocky Mountains of Alberta and British Columbia to Montana and Idaho. Males have shortened wings like other members of the genus, but females are fully winged.
Emergence occurs in July and August.

Fig. 6.54. *Megarcys signata* nymph. CO: Routt Co., Bear River, 27.v.1995, B. Stark, J. Parham, C. Massey.

Fig. 6.55. *Megarcys signata* male. CO: Gilpin Co., South Boulder Creek, 28.vi.1995. B. Kontratieff.

Fig. 6.56. *Megarcys signata* female. CO: Gilpin Co., South Boulder Creek, 28.vi.1995, B. Kondratieff.

Fig. 6.57. *Megarcys watertoni* female. MT: Glacier Co., Baring Creek, 27.vii.1989, B. Stark.

Genus *Oconoperla*

Oconoperla includes a single uncommon southern Appalachian species, *O. innubila*. Nymphs live in splash zones under large, flat rocks of headwater streams and adults are usually found resting on vegetation near these sites. The male Xth tergum is cleft and the epiproct and lateral stylets are well developed. Nymphs are without gills and the three sided egg is adorned with scales arranged in hexagonal patterns.

Oconoperla innubila (Needham & Claassen)

Adult length 0.6-0.7 inches. Distribution Tennessee and the Carolinas. This is a small, dark, robust perlodine with a yellow spot behind the ocelli.

Emergence occurs in May and June.

Fig. 6.58. *Oconoperla innubila* nymph. NC: Macon Co., Robin Branch, 25.v.1993, B. Stark, R. Simmons, D. Kelly.

Fig. 6.59. *Oconoperla innubila* male. NC: Jackson Co., Mull Creek, 23.v.1993, B. Kondratieff, F. Kirchner.

Genus *Oroperla*

Oroperla includes only the uncommon and unusual species, *O. barbara*, known from a few sites in the Sierra Nevada of California. This genus is easily recognized by the abundance of long finger-like gills on the neck, thorax, abdomen and submentum; the three pairs of thoracic gills are double and there are seven pairs of abdominal gills. The male Xth tergum is cleft and the egg is circular in cross section.

Oroperla barbara Needham

Adult length 1.0-1.2 inches. Distribution Sierra Nevada of California. Adults of this large species are black with a yellow pigment spot behind the ocelli. Most specimens of this species are from the upper reaches of the Yuba and American River drainages. This species has the distinction of being the only American species originally described from a nymphal specimen.

Emergence occurs in May and June.

Fig. 6.60. *Oroperla barbara* female. CA: Plumas Co., Rice Creek, 30.v.1991, R. Baumann, B. Stark, C. Henderson.

Fig. 6.61. *Osobenus yakimae* female. CA: El Dorado Co., North Cosumnes River, 21.vi.1995, R. Bottorff.

Genus *Osobenus*

Osobenus is represented by a single, western species, *O. yakimae*. Gills are absent and the male 10th tergum is cleft. The epiproct consists of an upturned dorsal sclerite surmounting a basal, bulbous structure. The eggs are somewhat turtle shaped but the median keel is well developed giving the egg a 3-sided appearance.

Osobenus yakimae (Hoppe)

Adult length 0.6-0.7 inches. Distribution western North America from British Columbia to California. Adults are pale brown and there is a broad yellow pronotal stripe. Males have a lobe on sternum VII and the female subgenital plate is a large parabolic structure.

Emergence occurs from May through July.

Genus *Perlinodes*

Only the distinctive western species, *P. aurea*, is known for this genus. Long finger-like gills occur on the submentum, neck and each thoracic segment and males have a large forked process on the 7th tergum. The male Xth tergum is cleft, the epiproct is well developed but the lateral stylets do not project beyond the cowl of the epiproct. Eggs are circular in cross section.

Perlinodes aurea (Smith)

Adult length 0.8-1.1 inches. Distribution western North America from Montana and Washington to California. The brown adults are usually found in drifts or hiding under streamside objects by day.

Emergence occurs from April through June.

Fig. 6.62. *Perlinodes aurea* male. CA: Plumas Co., Rice Creek, 30.v.1991, B. Stark, R. Baumann, C. Henderson.

Genus *Pictetiella*

This genus includes a single uncommon North American species, *P. expansa* (Banks), found in the Rocky Mountains. Adults bear short submental gills and there are no lateral stylets on the male genitalia. No photographs are available for this group.

Genus *Remenus*

Remenus includes three small perlodine stoneflies found in the Appalachians. *R. bilobatus* (Needham & Claassen) occurs from New York to Alabama, whereas *R. duffieldi* Kondratieff & Nelson and *R. kirchneri* Kondratieff & Nelson are known from Georgia and West Virginia, respectively. Adults lack submental gills and the males lack lateral stylets. Nymphs have a single large maxillary tooth. No photographs are available for this group.

Genus *Rickera*

This genus includes an uncommon western species, *R. sorpta* (Needham & Claassen). Adults of this species resemble those of *Kogotus* and *Baumannella* but males lack a cleft Xth tergum. No photographs are available for this group.

Genus *Salmoperla*

Salmoperla is another genus represented by a single uncommon species, *S. sylvanica*. Finger-like gills occur on the submentum and each thoracic segment; those on the prothorax are stubby and single but the other thoracic gills are long and double. Males have a cleft Xth tergum with well developed epiproct and the eggs are circular in cross section.

Salmoperla sylvanica Baumann & Lauck

Adult length 1.1-1.4 inches. Distribution northern Coast Range of California. Adults are brown with a conspicuous yellow pattern. The few adults collected were found resting on streamside vegetation and bridge structures.

Emergence occurs in May and June.

Fig. 6.63. *Salmoperla sylvanica* male. CA: Humboldt Co., Slide Creek, 31.v.1991, R. Baumann, B. Stark, C. Henderson.

Genus *Setvena*

Setvena includes three uncommon western species usually found in small streams or associated with springs. Finger-like gills are present on the submentum and meso and metathoracic segments but prothoracic gills are absent. The male Xth tergum is cleft, the epiproct and lateral stylets are well developed and eggs are circular in outline and lack a collar.

Setvena tibialis (Banks)

Adult length 0.8-1.1 inches. Distribution British Columbia to Oregon. The brown adults are found in crevices, under bark and resting on streamside vegetation.

Emergence occurs in May and June.

Fig. 6.64. *Setvena tibialis* male. OR: Hood River Co., Culvert Creek, 5.vi.1991, B. Stark, R. Baumann, C. Henderson.

Fig. 6.65. *Setvena wahkeena* male. OR: Multnomah Co., Wahkeena Falls, 5.vii.1993, G. Fiala.

Setvena wahkeena Stewart & Stanger

Adult length 0.8-1.1 inches. Distribution Oregon. This species is currently known only from the Columbia River gorge.

Emergence occurs in June and July.

Genus *Skwala*

Skwala includes two species in western North America and a small contingent in the eastern Palearctic region. Nymphs and adults have long submental gills but other gills are absent. The male Xth tergum is cleft and the epiproct and lateral stylets are well developed. Eggs are circular in cross section. Males are often short winged and hide under rocks and streamside debris.

Skwala americana (Klapalek)

Adult length 0.7-0.9 inches. Distribution western North America from British Columbia and Manitoba to California and New Mexico. Males of this species have shorter hemitergal lobes than *S. curvata*, the other American species.

Emergence occurs from April through June.

Genus *Susulus*

This genus includes the uncommon California species, *S. venustus* (Jewett). *Susulus* adults resemble those of *Chernokrilus* in general appearance but have long, slender submental gills and also differ in lacking a distinct lobe on sternum VII in the male. Additionally, the two genera differ in the shape of the mesosternal ridge pattern. No photographs are available for this group.

[Clockwise from upper left]

Fig. 6.66. *Skwala americana* nymph. CO: Jackson Co., Michigan River, 17.v.1991, B. Stark, S. Szczytko.

Fig. 6.67. *Skwala americana* male. CO: Larimer Co., Cache la Poudre River, 6.iv.1993, B. Kondratieff.

Fig. 6.68. *Skwala americana* female. UT: Salt Lake Co., Mill Creek, 26.v.1991, B. Stark, C. Henderson.

Genus *Yugus*

Two eastern Nearctic species currently comprise this genus and in medium size creeks of the southern Appalachians they can be locally abundant. Submental gills are short or absent and the male Xth tergum is cleft. The epiproct is well developed, eggs are three sided and lateral stylets are absent. The male VIIth sternum bears a broad lobe.

Yugus bulbosus (Frison)

Adult length 0.6-0.7 inches. Distribution Pennsylvania to Georgia and South Carolina. Adults are brown or black patterned with yellow. The epiproct is bulbous apically.

Emergence occurs from May through June.

Fig. 6.69. *Yugus bulbosus* female. NC: Haywood Co., North Fork Cove Creek, 23.v.1993, B. Kondratieff, F. Kirchner.

CHAPTER 7

FAMILY CHLOROPERLIDAE—THE SALLFLIES

Sallflies are typically small, slender bodied, yellow or green stoneflies, but a few dark species are included in the family. Wing venation is reduced, particularly in the number of crossveins, and in the size of the hindwing anal area. Nymphs are slender and brown, without distinctive patterns, and gills are absent. Many chloroperlid nymphs burrow deeply into the sand and gravel substrata making them difficult to collect, while the adults are readily found on streamside vegetation. Fly patterns modeled after adult chloroperlids are often referred to as "yellow sallies" or as "little yellows" or "little greens". Thirteen chloroperlid genera occur in North America.

Genus *Alaskaperla*

This genus includes a single uncommon species, *A. ovibovis* (Ricker), known from Alaska and Northwest Territory. Adults are yellow with darkened pronotal margins and a dark median abdominal stripe. They are generally similar to adult *Suwallia* but the male hemiterga lack finger-like lobes and the epiproct is a longer and more prominent tab-like structure. Females may be distinguished from *Suwallia* by the presence of sclerotized mandibles and spinule lining in the vagina. No photographs are available for this group.

Genus *Alloperla*

Twenty nine species of these slender green or yellow sallflies occur in North America primarily in mountainous regions. Most adults lack dark markings on the body, and the males have small epiprocts, broadly rounded hemitergal lobes, and lack other abdominal processes. The apical cercal segments of nymphs are fringed with long setae. Usually only male *Alloperla* can be reliably identified to species.

Alloperla atlantica Baumann

Adult length 0.4-0.5 inches. Distribution Maritime provinces and Minnesota to South Carolina and Alabama. *A. atlantica* adults are yellow-green. Males have a long, slender epiproct which tapers to a smooth, pointed apex. The species is similar to *A. imbecilla* but males of that species have small lateral serrations on the epiproct tip.

Emergence occurs from May to July.

Fig. 7.1. *Alloperla atlantica* male. NC: Swain Co., Nantahala River, 27.v.1994, B. Stark, S. Szczytko, J. Sandberg.

Fig. 7.2. *Alloperla nanina* male. NC: Jackson Co., Mull Creek, 26.v.1993, B. Stark, R. Simmons, D. Kelly.

Alloperla nanina Banks

Adult length 0.3-0.4 inches. Distribution eastern North America from New York to Georgia. *A. nanina* adults are olive green, but have a dark abdominal stripe. Males have a short apical section of the epiproct which is serrate along the ventral margin.

Emergence occurs in May and June.

Alloperla natchez Surdick and Stark

Adult length 0.3-0.5 inches. Distribution southwest Mississippi. *A. natchez* adults vary in coloration from bright lemon yellow to olive green within the same population. Males have a long slender epiproct similar to that of *A. atlantica*, but the apex is truncate and notched.

Emergence occurs in April and May.

Fig. 7.3. *Alloperla natchez* females. MS: Claiborne Co., Ragsdale Creek, 11.iv.1993, B. Stark.

Fig. 7.4. *Alloperla natchez* yellow form female. MS: Claiborne Co., Ragsdale Creek, 11.iv.1993, B. Stark.

Alloperla severa (Hagen)

Adult length 0.4-0.5 inches. Distribution western North America from Alaska to California and Colorado. Adults of this species are bright green with no dark abdominal markings. Males have a small rounded apical section of the epiproct and females have a wide, triangular subgenital plate which projects beyond the posterior margin of segment IX.

Emergence occurs from May to September.

Fig. 7.5. *Alloperla severa* female. OR: Tillamook Co., Kilchis River, 5.vi.1991, B. Stark, R. Baumann, C. Henderson.

Fig. 7.6. *Alloperla usa* female. NC: Macon Co., Wayah Creek, 12.vi.1992, B. Stark.

Alloperla usa Ricker

Adult length 0.4-0.6 inches. Distribution eastern North America from Ohio and Pennsylvania to Alabama and South Carolina. *A. usa* is one of the true "greenies" of eastern North America. Males have an oval apical section to the epiproct with an upturned and narrowly notched apex. Most of the dorsal epiproct surface is covered with a dense patch of red-brown setae.

Emergence occurs in May and June.

Genus *Bisancora*

This genus includes two uncommon California species, *B. pastina* (Jewett) and *B. rutriformis* Surdick. Adults are small (4-6 mm), tan stoneflies with a general similarity to *Alloperla*. Males have the epiproct tip flattened and curled, and the female subgenital plate is thickened and scalloped along the posterior margin. No photographs are available for this group.

Genus *Haploperla*

Four species of these small yellow sallflies occur in North America with three eastern and one western species currently recognized. Adults lack an anal fold on the rear wing, and some species have an obscure brown abdominal stripe. Males have simple tab-like epiprocts and females have short rounded subgenital plates. Species in this genus were formerly placed in genus *Hastaperla*.

Haploperla brevis (Banks)

Adult size 0.25-0.4 inches. Distribution eastern North America from New Brunswick and Saskatchewan to South Carolina and Oklahoma. Adults of this species are bright yellow and lack a dorsal stripe. Males have a broadly triangular epiproct.

Emergence occurs from April through June.

Fig. 7.7. *Haploperla brevis* female. WI: Oneida Co., Bearskin Creek, 20.viii.1992, C. R. Nelson.

Fig. 7.8. *Haploperla chukcho* female. MS: Claiborne Co., Ragsdale Creek, 11.iv.1993, B. Stark.

Haploperla chukcho (Surdick and Stark)

Adult size 0.25-0.35 inches. Distribution southwest Mississippi. Adults of this species are yellow to yellow-green with an obscure brown abdominal stripe and brown veins in the center of the wings. The male epiproct is longer and narrower than that of *H. brevis*.

Emergence occurs in March and April.

Genus *Kathroperla*

Two species of these large, slender head sallflies occur in western North America. Adults have long yellow-brown heads with black margins and the pronotum is striped with yellow and black. Both adults and nymphs are recognized by the long narrow head with the eyes located at about midlength. Males have a well developed vesicle on abdominal segment IX.

Kathroperla takhoma Stark and Surdick

Adult length 0.8-1.1 inches. Known distribution Cascades and Coastal Ranges from Washington to northern California. *K. takhoma* is quite similar to *K. perdita*, which is found on the west coast and in the northern Rockies, but *K. takhoma* has more definitive striping on the head and thorax in addition to genitalic and egg differences. Male *K. takhoma* have the vesicle rounded apically and strongly narrowed basally, and the basal cercal segments are at least 3 times long as wide. Female subgenital plates reach the posterior margin of segment IX, and the eggs are covered with irregular, scattered tubercles. *K. perdita* eggs have these tubercles organized into striations.

Emergence occurs from April through May.

Fig. 7.9. *Kathroperla takhoma* female. CA: Humboldt Co., Slide Creek, 31.v.1991, B. Stark, R. Baumann, C. Henderson.

Genus *Neaviperla*

This genus includes a single uncommon species, *N. forcipata* (Neave), known from Montana and Washington to Alaska. Adults are generally similar to *Suwallia* but in both sexes the basal cercal segment is at least three times long as wide. In males, this segment bears a basal spine and is swollen apically. The male epiproct is also quite large and unusually shaped by chloroperlid standards. No photographs are available for this group.

Genus *Paraperla*

Paraperla currently includes two Nearctic species, *P. frontalis* and *P. wilsoni*. The adults are dark and have the eyes set forward from the hind margins of the head. Males have a slender epiproct recessed into the partially cleft Xth tergum.

Paraperla frontalis (Banks)

Adult length 0.5-0.7 inches. Distribution Alaska and South Dakota to California and New Mexico. Males of this species have lateral stylets and the epiproct tip is often sharply bent.

Emergence occurs from April through July.

Fig. 7.10. *Paraperla frontalis* female. CA: El Dorado Co., Sopiago Creek, 3.v.1995, R. Bottorff.

Genus *Plumiperla*

Two species of these striped sallflies occur in western North America. Adults are yellow with narrow, dark, median pronotal and abdominal stripes. Males have small epiprocts and females have broadly triangular subgenital plates. Adults and nymphs are quite similar to *Triznaka* species but *Triznaka* adults have dark pigment spots on the head which *Plumiperla* adults lack.

Plumiperla diversa (Frison)

Adult length 0.4-0.6 inches. Distribution western North America from Alaska to California and New Mexico. Males have a tab-like, almost quadrate epiproct apex, which distinguishes this species from *P. spinosa*. *P. spinosa*, currently known only from the Sierras north of Lake Tahoe, has a pointed epiproct tip.

Emergence occurs from May through July.

Fig. 7.11. *Plumiperla diversa* female. MT: Carbon Co., Rock Creek, 23.vii.1989, B. Stark.

Genus *Rasvena*

This genus is represented by a single uncommon eastern species, *R. terna* (Frison). Adults are small (4-5 mm), pale sallflies with a general similarity to *Haploperla*. These genera are usually distinguished on the basis of wing morphology; *Haploperla* adults have the anal area and fold undeveloped, whereas these are present and distinct in *Rasvena*. No photographs are available for this group.

Genus *Suwallia*

Six species of yellow sallflies are known currently for North America. Five of these occur in the west and a single species, *S. marginata* is known in the east. Adults are yellow with dark pronotal margins and abdominal stripes. Males usually have small epiprocts and small finger-like hemitergal lobes, and females have relatively large subgenital plates.

Suwallia sp.

Adult length 0.4-0.6 inches. Distribution California. This apparently undescribed species can be distinguished from other members of the genus by careful examination of setal arrangements on the internal male genitalia.

Emergence occurs in July and August.

Fig. 7.12. *Suwallia* sp. female. CA: Alpine Co., West Carson River, 27.vii.1995, R. Bottorff.

Genus *Sweltsa*

Twenty-seven species of these yellow or bronze sallflies occur in North America. Adults typically have dark pigment on the head and thorax and usually an abdominal stripe is present. Males have relatively large epiprocts and in many species, a small dorsal process is located on segment IX.

Sweltsa coloradensis (Banks)

Adult length 0.4-0.6 inches. Distribution western North America from the Yukon to California and New Mexico. Adults display dark markings on the head and pronotal disc and the males have a broadly flattened epiproct with upturned tip. In both these features *S. coloradensis* resembles *S. lamba* but the latter species has a leaf-like appendage on the internal male genitalia and this structure is absent in *S. coloradensis*.

Emergence is recorded from April through August.

Fig. 7.13. *Sweltsa coloradensis* nymph. AZ: Cochise Co., Ruckes Creek, 25.v.1993, C. R. Nelson.

Fig. 7.14. *Sweltsa coloradensis* female. AZ: Graham Co., Marjilda Creek, 27.v.1993, C. R. Nelson.

Sweltsa hondo Baumann & Jacobi

Adult length 0.4-0.6 inches. Distribution New Mexico. This species is quite similar to *S. lamba*. Males are distinguished from this species by shape of the internal leaf-like structure and by subtle details of the epiproct. In *S. hondo* the epiproct abruptly narrows near the apex and forms a subapical truncate base from which the apical hook arises.

Emergence is recorded from June through August.

Fig. 7.15. *Sweltsa hondo* male. NM: Bernalillo Co., Las Huertas Creek, 26.v.1991, J. K. Gelhaus, C. R. Nelson.

Fig. 7.16. *Sweltsa lamba* female. CO: Larimer Co., Skin Gulch, 31.v.1993, B. Kondratieff.

Sweltsa lamba (Needham and Claassen)

Adult length 0.4-0.6 inches. Distribution Rocky Mountains from Idaho to New Mexico. Adults are characterized by a pattern of dark markings on the head and pronotum and by distinctive genitalia. Males have a broad epiproct with a prominent mid-dorsal carina. The apex is hooked and a small process is located on segment IX. The internal genitalia bears a short and wide leaf-like structure, and the female subgenital plate is broadly rounded. This species is similar to *S. gaufini* and *S. albertensis* and overlaps both in range.

Emergence occurs from May through September.

Sweltsa lateralis (Banks)

Adult length 0.3-0.4 inches. Reported distribution eastern North America from New Brunswick to South Carolina. Adults have the pronotum narrowly margined with black pigment, and a dark abdominal stripe is present. Males have a long epiproct with a slender recurved tip which is one of the most distinctive in the genus.

Emergence occurs in May and June.

Fig. 7.17. *Sweltsa lateralis* female. NC: Macon Co., Robin Branch, 25.v.1993, B. Stark, R. Simmons, D. Kelly.

Sweltsa townesi (Ricker)

Adult length 0.4-0.5 inches. Distribution Northern Sierra Nevada Mountains of California and Nevada. Adults have black, lateral pronotal margins and a small cleft process occurs on the male VIIIth tergum.

Emergence occurs from May through July.

Fig. 7.18. *Sweltsa townesi* male. CA: El Dorado Co., North Cosumnes River, 11.v.1995, R. Bottorff.

Fig. 7.19. *Sweltsa umbonata* female. CA: El Dorado Co., Tony Gulch, 11.v.1995, R. Bottorff.

Sweltsa umbonata Surdick

Adult length 0.4-0.6 inches. Distribution Northern Sierra Nevada Mountains of California. This species is in the *S. borealis* complex and is separated from other members of this group by epiproct shape and in females by shape of the subgenital plate lobes and particularly by the presence of a low longitudinal ridge on the plate.

Emergence occurs in May and June.

Genus *Triznaka*

Two species of these yellow and black patterned sallflies occur in western North America. Adults have both a dark median head patch and a dark median pronotal stripe. Males have small tab-shaped epiprocts and the female subgenital plate is large and entire.

Triznaka pintada (Ricker)

Adult length 0.4-0.6 inches. Distribution western North America from Washington and South Dakota to California and New Mexico. Both *T. pintada* and *T. signata* have median pronotal stripes but in *T. pintada* this stripe is only along the median suture and the pronotal rugosities are pigmented.

Emergence occurs from May through July.

Fig. 7.20. *Triznaka pintada* female. NM: Lincoln Co., Rio Bonito, 29.v.1995, B. Stark, C. Massey, K. Simpson.

Triznaka signata (Banks)

Adult length 0.4-0.6 inches. Distribution western North America from Alaska to New Mexico. Adults are usually recognized by the distinctive pronotal and head patterns. The median pronotal stripe, in particular, is much wider than in *T. pintada*.

Emergence occurs from May through July.

Fig. 7.21. *Triznaka signata* nymph. UT: Utah Co., 12 miles E. Thistle, 14.vii.1995, C. Nelson.

Fig. 7.22. *Triznaka signata* female. CO: Larimer Co., Lone Pine Creek, 7.vii.1993, B. Kondratieff.

Genus *Utaperla*

This genus is represented by an uncommon western species, *U. sopladora* Ricker, and a northeastern species, *U. gaspesiana* Harper & Roy. The small dark adults have a somewhat quadrate head posterior to the eyes. No photographs are available for this group.

CHAPTER 8

FAMILY CAPNIIDAE—THE WINTER STONEFLIES

The winter stoneflies are small, dark insects which emerge during the harshest, coldest parts of the season. They are often found actively crawling around on snow and ice when air temperatures are hovering at or below zero degrees Celsius. They are the most species rich family of stoneflies in North America with 150 species known currently. Capniids in North America can be found from coast to coast in the more mountainous areas from north of the Arctic Circle to the Sierra Madre Occidental of Sonora and Chihuahua, Mexico. It is interesting to note that a broad band of land in the prairie regions lacks capniid species.

Capniids are small stoneflies which are dark brown or black as adults. Wing length varies from fully winged to apterous and all genera in the family in North America have representative species with shortened wings in at least one of the sexes. Additionally, wing length varies among populations of some species. Specimens exhibit all degrees of wing shortening, but are more or less constant for wing length within each population. Males are more likely to have shortened wings than are females, but wing shortening alone is not a reliable field character for determining the sex of the individual. Research into genetic control versus environmental control of wing length would without a doubt reveal many more interesting facts about these insects related to this question of general biological interest.

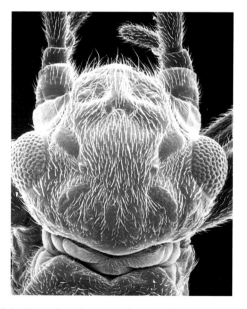

Fig. 8.1. Scanning electron micrograph, *Capnia lineata*, adult head in dorsal view. ID: Latah Co., Spring Valley Creek, 25.iv.1985, R. W. Baumann, C. R. Nelson.

In the field, most capniids can be distinguished from other stoneflies by their small size, dark coloration, and long cerci. Two North American genera, *Eucapnopsis* and *Isocapnia* have some adults with somewhat shortened cerci, but still these cerci are longer than those found in the leuctrids and nemourids with which they might be confused. Capniid nymphs are brown or tan, usually without distinctive pigment patterns. As in the Leuctridae, they never have gills. The nymphs are difficult to separate from those of the Leuctridae on morphological grounds, but generally have a longer pleural fold on the abdomen (from segment 1-9) than do the leuctrids (from segment 1-7).

Fig. 8.2. Scanning electron micrograph, *Capnia inyo*, adult male epiproct in lateral view. CA: Inyo Co., Lone Pine Creek, 25.i.1985, R. W. Baumann, C. R. Nelson.

Species new to science are regularly discovered among the winter stoneflies, in part because of their habits of winter emergence when most stonefly hunters are busy with other tasks but at least partially because endemism (distribution over a small range) is rampant in this group. Several species are known only from single localities or within a single small watershed.

Capniid species can be found in a variety of flowing water habitats with some species found in headwater springs and others in big, slow moving rivers. The largest number of species, however, occur in streams small enough to cross in a few steps. A small number of species live in cold, pristine mountain lakes which have considerable wave action, but most of these are also found in flowing waters surrounding the lakes. One of these lake-dwelling species, *Capnia lacustra* Jewett, attracts considerable attention because it is the only fully aquatic stonefly species in the world. This species passes through its entire life history deep in Lake Tahoe. Adults and nymphs of *C. lacustra* have been collected from dredge samples at depths ranging from 100 to 422 feet. Unfortunately all these specimens were collected in the 1960s and despite considerable effort, no specimens have been collected in recent years. Another capniid in Lake Tahoe, *Utacapnia tahoensis* (Nebeker & Gaufin), is still common on the lake's rocky wave-washed shores. This species differs from *C. lacustra* in many ways, most notably in that the adults are terrestrial. Additional field research is necessary to determine if *C. lacustra* still exists in Lake Tahoe. Additional lake dwelling forms are scattered across northern North America, Europe and Asia. Lake Baikal, an amazingly deep and clear water body in central Asia is home to several unique capniid species. Other deep, pristine mountain lakes, such as Crater Lake in Oregon need to be searched for winter stoneflies which might share the odd condition of aquatic adulthood found in *C. lacustra*.

The nymphs of capniids are slender and brown. They may be distinguished from the related Leuctridae by a slightly stockier appearance and an incomplete lateral groove on the abdomen. No gills are present on nymphs of either of these families, perhaps because their small size yields a high surface area to volume ratio which allows enough oxygen to simply pass through the body wall from their highly oxygenated cold-water habitats. The species diversity of capniids is richest in mountainous regions of the middle latitudes (35 to 50 degrees N) of the northern continents.

The life history of the nymphs is interesting in that they all seem to be hyporheic, that is to say they inhabit the flow of water in streams beneath the bottom substrates. The nymphs of capniids are not regularly sampled by most stream ecologists because they spend most of the year deep in the gravel and cobble below the stream where they feed on detritus. Such detritivorous habits make them an important base of the food webs in these relatively energy-poor hyporheic zones. Predators also inhabit this zone, the more common in northern regions being chloroperlid stoneflies in the genera *Paraperla* and *Kathroperla*. The capniids of more southerly distribution are free from predation by these chloroperlids. These hyporheic habits of stoneflies in these genera and *Isocapnia* were originally brought to light by Stanford & Gaufin (1974) where they found the nymphs from depths of at least 4.2 meters below the stream bottom and up to 50 meters laterally from the stream channel. This discovery was made when stonefly nymphs were appearing in the domestic water of users in Eureka, Montana after the installation of a new culinary system. Hundreds of nymphs were obtained by pumping from the supply galleries for as little as 30 minutes, an indication of the huge numbers that must exist in these inaccessible habitats. Still, imagine the surprise (and no doubt disgust) of residents when they found pretty little insects crawling around in their glasses of water! The local problem was partially alleviated by the installation of screen mesh at the delivery end of the water treatment facilities. This eliminated whole insects from entering the supply, but water pressure dismembered the nymphs such that minute insect parts then were detected in the water. Actually, if it were inevitable to have insects crawling around in a drink we would clearly choose stoneflies. This is because they are among the least tolerant of insects with respect to pollution, disappearing from streams where even low doses of toxic substances have been introduced.

Why these insects emerge in the middle of winter is an interesting question because it would seem more intuitive to emerge when terrestrial conditions are not so harsh. It may well be that predation of adults is lower in the winter because major predators of the stoneflies, such as migratory birds, spiders, and ants are not winter active. Further field research examining this question is needed before this answer is little more than speculation.

Genus *Allocapnia*

The genus *Allocapnia* is one of the largest in the Capniidae with 41 species in North America. This genus ranges from the eastern seaboard of North America west to the Great Plains. Several species have rather limited ranges while others are quite widely distributed. These attributes have made these fascinating stoneflies the object of several important studies of biogeography as it relates to earth history, summarized well in Ross and Ricker (1971). The complex, two-limbed male epiproct and patterns of the female subgenital plate are useful in separating the species in this genus. The keys and diagnoses in Ross and Ricker (1971) should be carefully consulted when identifying members of this genus.

The adults of *Allocapnia* are small, ranging from about 0.2-0.4 inches, and are particularly well-suited to being collected from concrete pillars and bridges across clean streams during the winter months. It is common to collect several species of *Allocapnia* at a single location on the same day. Adults can be extremely abundant during parts of their emergence period. Adults can also be collected with regularity high on streamside trees.

Allocapnia fumosa Ross

Adult length 0.2-0.4 inches. This species is a narrow endemic, it occurs only in a few fairly large, fast, rocky streams and small rivers in or close to the Great Smoky Mountains of the southern Appalachians (Ross & Ricker 1971). It is quite closely related to *A. granulata* and identification of this species requires observation of the setose processes adjacent to the dorsal process of abdominal segment eight.

Emergence is recorded from late December through early January, quite a narrow window in which to capture the adults.

Fig. 8.3. *Allocapnia fumosa* female. NC: Macon Co., Wayah Bald, 5.i.1993, B. P. Stark.

Allocapnia granulata (Claassen)

Adult length 0.2-0.4 inches. This is one of the widely distributed members of the genus occurring throughout much of eastern North America, generally south of the Great Lakes in the north and northward from the Coastal Plain at the southern margin of its range. It extends further to the southwest than any other member of the genus, as far west as the Wichita Mountains of Oklahoma. It is commonly found in larger and more sluggish streams and rivers than most members of the genus. Identification of this species requires observation of the male genitalic structures which are quite variable.

Emergence is recorded from early December through late April with earlier emergences in the southern portion of the range and later emergences in the north.

Fig. 8.4. *Allocapnia granulata*. WI: Lincoln Co. Prairie River, 7.iii.1990, S. W. Szczytko, J. Dimick.

Allocapnia virginiana Frison

Adult length 0.2-0.4 inches. This species has a much narrower range than either of the two previous species. It has been collected from streams draining the eastern slope of the Appalachian Mountains and a few locations to the south on the Coastal Plain. It has not been collected in the main drainages of the Mississippi River system nor in the Interior Highlands. It is commonly found in rapid, clear streams with rocky or gravel bottoms.

Emergence is recorded from late November through late February.

Fig. 8.5. *Allocapnia virginiana* female. MS: Simpson Co., Rials Creek, 19.xii.1992, B. P. Stark.

Genus *Bolshecapnia*

Bolshecapnia is currently recognized as a genus composed of six North American species in which the males have a ventral vesicle on the 9th sternum and are large in size. The variation, however, in epiproct morphology of the males and subgenital plate configuration of the females indicates that this may be an artificial classification rather than one that reflects phylogeny. Indeed this genus should be studied in detail and revised to let the classification reflect more closely the relationships among species contained therein and other genera and species in the family. The relationships among members of this genus to some capniids from Asia and Europe needs careful attention.

Almost all the species in this genus have been collected only rarely, the exception being *B. spenceri* (Ricker) which has been collected abundantly at Iceberg Lake in Glacier National Park, Montana. Several species have been collected only in March, but others have been collected as late as August in northerly, high elevation settings. No photographs are available for this group.

Genus *Capnia*

The genus *Capnia* is the largest in the Capniidae with 52 species in North America and at least that many elsewhere. This genus ranges from coast to coast in North American but is particularly abundant and species rich west of the Great Plains. The genus consists of several widely ranging species as well as numerous species which have very limited range distributions. Many species currently placed in the genus *Capnia* will undoubtedly be placed in more narrowly defined genera as more research is done with this important group. A beginning to a general understanding of the taxonomy of the genus in North America can be found in Nelson & Baumann (1989).

Fig. 8.6. *Capnia* sp. nymph, on skeletonized leaf. CO: Larimer Co., Young Gulch, 14.iii.1991, C. R. Nelson #5638, M. Harris.

The adults of *Capnia* are small, ranging from about 0.2-0.4 inches. The greatest diversity of species occurs in small to middle-sized streams which are cold, clear, and rocky bottomed. Different species in the genus emerge at different times as one moves up the stream continuum toward the headwaters. Several species have been collected on only one occasion. Like other members of the family the winter months are the time of adult emergence. Adults are frequently found in large numbers walking on snow and ice. Man-made structures, such as bridges, poles, and fences are often good places to find *Capnia*. One can commonly collect several species of *Capnia* at a single time and place.

Capnia confusa Claassen

Adult length 0.2-0.4 inches. This is one of the widely distributed members of the genus occurring throughout much of western North America, particularly in the inland mountain ranges. It is commonly found in both larger rivers and small streams. Perhaps this tolerance for a range of habitat types has led to its ecological success as a widespread species. *Capnia confusa* is often the last capniid of the season to be caught in a given stream. The males have simple tube-like epiprocts which might be confused for a variety of species in the genus, but the female's medial projection on the hind margin of the seventh abdominal sternum is unique for the genus and makes identification rather simple. The identification of this species, and other North American species, should be made in consultation with keys and diagnoses found in Nelson and Baumann (1989).

Emergence is recorded from early January through early August. The late season records are from high elevations nearer the North Pole.

Fig. 8.7. *Capnia confusa* on granite. CO: Larimer Co., Cache la Poudre River, 19.v.1991, C. R. Nelson #5672.

Capnia decepta (Banks)

Adult length 0.2-0.4 inches. This is another widely distributed member of the genus occurring throughout many of the mountain ranges of southwestern North America. It is generally limited to small, well-oxygenated streams within its range, but seems to be more tolerant of warmer water than are most other members of the genus. This species can be very abundant in streams along the Front Range of the Rocky Mountains in Colorado as well as from the isolated "island" mountain ranges of New Mexico, Arizona, Nevada, Baja California, and Chihuahua. *Capnia decepta* ranges as far south into Mexico as any member of the family. This species belongs to a group in the genus which have an epiproct which resembles the head of a duck in lateral view. The exact spine patterns and characteristic shapes given in Nelson and Baumann (1989) must be determined to properly identify the individual species in this group. In the field one can sometimes see the broad orange epiproct of this species when held up to the sun.

Emergence is recorded from late December to late April.

Fig. 8.8. *Capnia decepta* on dead leaf. CO: Larimer Co., Young Gulch 14.iii.1991, C. R. Nelson #5638, M. Harris.

Fig. 8.9. *Capnia decepta* on snow. CO: Larimer Co., Young Gulch 14.iii.1991, C. R. Nelson #5638, M. Harris.

Capnia gracilaria Claassen

Adult length 0.2-0.4 inches. This species is the most frequently collected species in the genus. It is commonly found in rapid, clear, streams and rivers with gravelly and rocky substrates. The species is particularly common in the inland portions of the Rocky Mountains, but scattered records of this

Fig. 8.10. *Capnia gracilaria* on ice crystal. CO: Larimer Co., Young Gulch 14.iii.1991, C. R. Nelson #5638, M. Harris.

species have been taken from the coastal ranges of California as well as isolated mountain tops in New Mexico and the Sierra San Pedro Martir of Baja California. It is somewhat surprising that this common and widespread species has not been taken in Arizona. The evenly curved, thin, tubular epiproct of the males is distinctive for this species. The females are virtually indistinguishable from those of several other species in the genus.

Emergence is recorded from late December through mid July. As is usual for the family, late season records are from the highest elevations where spring comes late and winter comes early.

Capnia nana Claassen

Adult length 0.2-0.4 inches. This species is one of the more frequently collected species in the genus. It is commonly found in spring runs in its range, but can be found in smaller populations in somewhat larger streams and rivers with gravelly and rocky substrates and clear flows. The species is particularly common in the northern mountains of Utah in the central Rocky Mountains, but scattered records of this species have been taken throughout the inland Rocky Mountains all the way to Alaska. The dorsal view of the epiproct of the males is particularly distinctive for this species: it curves outward at the base, then narrows moving distally then recurves out slightly at the apex such that it resembles a rosebud vase. The females are distinguishable from others in the genus in that the subgenital plate bears a darkened triangle with the base on the hind margin of the plate and the apex directed anteriorly. The apex of the darkened triangle can be fainter than the base. Two subspecies have been recognized in the species with the southern form (*nana wasatchae*) having a stouter epiproct than the typical northern form (*nana nana*). Females of the two subspecies are not readily distinguishable. Fishermen on the Logan River in northern Utah tie a small black imitation of this species (could be other capniids as well) when seeking the winter active mountain whitefish, the pattern works for trout as well.

Emergence is recorded from November to June, with early and late emergences coming from springs where water temperatures are more even throughout the year than those of surrounding surface flow.

Fig. 8.11. *Capnia nana wasatchae* female. UT: Utah Co., Left hand of South Fork of American Fork River, 17.vii.1995, C. R. & A. L. Nelson #6236.

Capnia pileata Jewett

Adult length 0.2-0.4 inches. This species has quite a narrow distribution pattern in the coastal mountains ranging from Portland, Oregon south to the northern third of coastal California. It is limited to small, well-oxygenated streams within its range. This species still occurs in the small creek in suburban Portland from which it was originally described, despite the heavy urbanization of the area which has polluted other nearby creeks. This species belongs to the same group in the genus as *Capnia decepta*, both have epiprocts which resemble duck heads. The epiproct of this species has a more angular "forehead" than that of *C. decepta* but species determinations should be made using Nelson and Baumann (1989).

Emergence is recorded from January to April.

Fig. 8.12. *Capnia pileata* on leaf. CA: Colusa Co., Mill Creek, 20.i.1989, C. R. Nelson #5320, W. D. Shepard.

Capnia vernalis Newport

Adult length 0.2-0.4 inches. This species ranges quite widely in the interior of western North America. This species has disjunct populations, however, in isolated regions far to the east along the eastern seaboard in Canada as well as a few localities near the shores of Lake Superior and Ungava Bay in Quebec. The widely separated localities from which the species has been collected represent an enigma for biogeographers. The best explanation, perhaps, for these disjunct populations, probably relates to differential survival and colonization during and immediately after the Pleistocene glaciations. *Capnia vernalis* occurs in very large rivers, as well as a few smaller ones. They can be extremely abundant during their emergences and ecologists ignoring these hatches are certainly underestimating productivity in the rivers where this species occurs. One of us (CRN) has collected hundreds of this species per square foot along the Green River in Wyoming.

The epiproct of this species is a rather narrow tube divided into a thicker basal section and a much narrowed distal portion. No other capniid has such an epiproct.

This species emerges with the latest of capniids coming from a given stream. Emergence is recorded February to July.

Fig. 8.13. *Capnia vernalis*. WY: Lincoln Co. Green River at Names Hill, 9.iv.1985, R. W. Baumann, C. R. Nelson.

Genus *Capnura*

This strictly North American genus consists of seven species. Six of these species have ranges limited to small portions of the west and a single, more widespread species, *Capnura manitoba,* occurs in the east. Members of the genus are slightly larger than the more common *Capnia* with which they are sometimes collected. They can be separated from *Capnia* on the basis of the epiproct which is divided into an upper and a lower limb. Neither of these limbs is laterally divided in *Capnura* as it is in *Utacapnia* and sometimes *Allocapnia*. The lower limb is very short in some of the species and care must be taken not to overlook it. These stoneflies are not found in high mountains but are encountered in small and ephemeral streams draining foothill regions. A few records of *Capnura manitoba* are from prairie regions lacking much topological relief. This contrasts with most other capniids which typically inhabit more mountainous regions.

Males in the genus typically show moderate to extreme wing shortening while the females are universally fully winged.

Capnura wanica Frison

Adult length 0.3-0.6 inches. This species can be found in the foothills of the Front Range of the Rocky Mountains, a few localities on the Colorado Plateau, and scattered in the Great Basin of western North America. *Capnura wanica* occurs in medium sized rivers and small streams. They can be extremely abundant during their emergences. Dead terrestrial vegetation, such as half submerged tumbleweeds, provide excellent emergence habitats for *C. wanica*.

The epiproct of this species consists of two tubes, with the much longer upper limb arching uniformly above the terminal segments of the abdomen. It is quite similar to *Capnura intermontana* Nelson & Baumann, which has less of an arch to the upper limb. Emergence is recorded December to April.

Fig. 8.14. *Capnura wanica* male. CO: Larimer Co., Redstone Creek 16.iii.1991, C. R. Nelson #5639, M. Harris.

Genus *Eucapnopsis*

This genus contains species in both western North America and eastern Asia. The single North American species is widespread in the west. The adults of *Eucapnopsis* are strange within the Capniidae in having shortened cerci, consisting of fewer than eleven segments. The shortening of the cerci is a result of breakage of the terminal cercal segments when the nymph transforms into adult. These small stoneflies are typically late winter, early spring emergers overlapping in emergence time with the last members of the genus *Capnia*. *Eucapnopsis* in North America are readily identified by their dark brown wings (compared to black in most other capniids) which are held flatter than other genera in the family. At a quick glance they resemble small leuctrids without curled wing margins. Also, members of this genus move more methodically, like leuctrids, than do most other capniids. They are closely related to *Isocapnia* and can be separated from *Isocapnia vedderensis* (Ricker) only on close examination of the terminal segments of the male abdomen.

Eucapnopsis brevicauda Claassen

Adult length 0.2-0.4 inches. This species ranges broadly in western North America, having been recorded in most of the major mountain ranges. It is easily collected from stream side leaf and debris packs. The males are very small, the smallest of capniids in North America. The species superficially resembles *Isocapnia vedderensis*, from which it can be separated by its globular, but forward-directed epiproct. The epiproct of *Isocapnia vedderensis* is much narrower and directed posteriorly or at most vertically.

This species emerges with the latest of capniids coming from a particular stream. Emergence has been recorded from February to July.

Fig. 8.15. *Eucapnopsis brevicauda* on granite. NM: Lincoln Co., Rio Bonito, 29.v.1995, B. P. Stark.

Genus *Isocapnia*

This genus contains the largest species of the family as well as some of the smallest. Some species, such as *I. crinita* (Needham & Claassen) and *I. missouri* Ricker, are unique in having large and dwarf forms which coincide in emergence times. The genus is widespread in the mid-northern latitudes of both western North America and eastern Asia, but is much less common that other genera in the family. As noted in the beginning of this chapter, the nymphs have been taken from wells drilled through the hyporheic zone of large rivers and from areas with surface flow. Nymphs of *Isocapnia* have long, vertical swimming hairs fringing the cerci. No photographs are available for this group.

Genus *Mesocapnia*

Mesocapnia occurs in North America and Asia and it appears to be the only capniid genus with a species (*M. variabilis* (Klapalek) occurring on both continents. The genus includes 15 North American and a few Asian species. Males have the epiproct tip constricted as a narrow spine; in most species the epiproct is tubular but in some the distal portion of the structure may be laterally broadened or inflated in any direction. Females almost always have a "nipple" on the midline of the subgenital plate which projects to the rear.

These stoneflies are found in higher mountains in the northern part of their range, but are more frequently encountered in small and ephemeral streams draining foothill regions in the south. The southeastern extent of the genus is in western Kansas and the Texas Panhandle. Some species have shortened wings, with shortening more noticeable in males than in females. Often *Mesocapnia* adults can be recognized in the field by the strong pigment pattern along the wing veins, but care must be employed in use of this feature. No photographs are available for this group.

Genus *Nemocapnia*

Nemocapnia has species in both eastern North America and eastern Asia. This is an uncommon biogeographic pattern. When these continents share a genus in common, it is more usual that the adjacent eastern Asia - western North America pattern be shown. The single North American species is widespread in the east from Quebec to Florida west to Illinois and Arkansas, but does not occur in New England. Separation of the genus from others in North America is based on details of the morphology of the thoracic sterna. Identification of the adults is perhaps more easily accomplished by examining the distinctive male epiproct or female subgenital plate of *N. carolina* and working backward to determine the genus. The nymphs of *Nemocapnia* have vertical swimming hairs on the cerci, a feature they share only with *Isocapnia* in the family. This vertical fringe is more sparse in *Nemocapnia* than in *Isocapnia*. In general appearance the nymph of *Nemocapnia* is shinier than those of *Isocapnia*.

Nemocapnia carolina Banks

Adult length 0.2-0.4 inches. Males have a rather simple tube for an epiproct that extends forward only to about the hind margin of the ninth tergite. The hind margin of the subgenital plate of the female is recessed from the margin of the sternite. The adults of *N. carolina* stay close to the water and are often abundant in loose partially submerged accumulations of leaves. They are not seen high in trees as is *Allocapnia*. Also unlike *Allocapnia*, they are somewhat sluggish when disturbed, perhaps relying on their cryptic coloration. Emergence for the day begins just as the sun rises. Seasonal emergence is from February to April.

Fig. 8.17. *Paracapnia angulata* male on willow flower. CO: Jackson Co., Michigan River, 19.v.1991, C. R. Nelson #5675.

Fig. 8.16. *Nemocapnia carolina* female. MS: Simpson Co., Rials Creek, xii.1994, B. P. Stark.

Genus *Paracapnia*

The genus *Paracapnia* can be found in both eastern and western North America as well as in eastern Asia. Five species have been recorded from North America, three unique to the west, one unique in the east, and the last, (*Paracapnia angulata* Hanson) widespread in the east with some records from streams draining the Rocky Mountains into the Mississippi River basin. Males have a thin, tubular epiproct which ends in a sharp point. A membranous sac often is protruding from near the apex of the epiproct. Females are difficult to separate from many others in the family, but they are generally hairier. Nymphs are readily separated from others in the family by their hairiness, which is even apparent in first instars. Males regularly have shortened wings but females are usually long winged. In long winged forms the straight base of vein R_1 is useful grouping females away from *Capnia* and with *Isocapnia*, *Eucapnopsis*, and *Nemocapnia*. The unusual laterally notched subgenital plate will usually serve to separate *Paracapnia* females from the other genera with a straight R_1 vein base. The general hairiness of the adults and nymphs is a very useful field attribute for recognizing this genus.

Paracapnia angulata Hanson

This species is the most widespread in the genus. It ranges from the eastern seaboard of southern Canada and the northern United States across the Great Lakes region into the prairie, then west to the foothills of the Rocky Mountains in southern Wyoming and northern Colorado. They emerge in moderately large numbers. Males in different populations have wings of various lengths: fixed within a population but variable between populations. Emergence of *Paracapnia angulata* has been recorded from January to May, again with earlier emergences at more southerly locations and lower elevations.

Genus *Utacapnia*

This strictly North American genus consists of 11 species. Ten of these species have ranges limited to the west and a single species, *U. labradora* (Ricker), occurs in eastern Canada. Members of the genus are slightly larger than the more common *Capnia* with which they are sometimes collected. They can be separated from *Capnia* on the basis of the epiproct which is divided into an upper and a lower limb, with the upper limb often divided into horn-like projections (but *U. nedia* lacks this forking of the upper limb). The lower limb is long to very long in all species. The lower limb curves upward from the base, a feature which helps distinguish the genus from *Capnura*. These stoneflies are found in high mountains with some species encountered on wave-washed rocky beaches of lakes. The narrowly endemic *U. tahoensis* can be extremely abundant on the rocky beaches of Lake Tahoe. Wing length varies greatly among populations of many of the species, with males typically more likely to have shortened wings than females. No photographs are available for this group.

CHAPTER 9

FAMILY LEUCTRIDAE—THE NEEDLEFLIES

Needleflies are slender, dark bodied stoneflies usually less than 12 mm in body length but *Megaleuctra* adults are at least 15 mm long. Adults have 1-segmented cerci, typically more than four intercubital crossveins in the forewings and the wings are rolled around the body at rest. Nymphs lack gills and the hind wingpads are parallel to the body axis. In both nymphs and adults the glossae and paraglossae are subequal in length and the mid tarsal segment is shorter than the basal segment. Many leuctrid species occur in the hyporhea of streams and are seldom collected as nymphs even though the adults may be common on streamside vegetation. Most leuctrid species emerge in the spring but *Zealeuctra* and a few southern *Leuctra* emerge in winter and other *Leuctra* emerge in late summer and fall. Eight genera and 55 leuctrid species are known for North America.

Genus *Calileuctra*

This genus includes two uncommon California species, *C. dobryi* Shepard & Baumann and *C. ephemera* Shepard & Baumann. Male abdominal tergum IX is dentate or lobed on the posterior margin and the vesicle on sternum IX is short and broad. The single male cercal segments are long and poorly sclerotized laterally. No photographs are available for this group.

Genus *Despaxia*

Despaxia includes a small species, *D. augusta* (Banks), found from California to Montana and Alaska in small streams, often at high elevations. Males lack a vesicle and dorsal lobes. The single male cercal segments are long and poorly sclerotized and a single pair of slender processes arise from the Xth sternum and curve upward over the abdominal apex. No photographs are available for this group.

Genus *Leuctra*

This genus is very diverse in Europe and includes 26 North American species making it the largest in the family. The adult male IXth abdominal tergum is not cleft but segments seven and eight may bear dorsal lobes. A slender vesicle is present on sternum nine and two pairs of long slender processes arise from the Xth sternum and curve upward over the abdominal apex. The shape of these structures, known as paraprocts, is important in species recognition in this group. In the hind wings, the crossvein joining the M and Cu veins is located before the point where the Cu vein forks.

Leuctra alexanderi Hanson

Adult length 0.3-0.4 inches. Distribution mountains of Kentucky, Tennessee, Virginia and West Virginia. Males have a bilobed process on the VIIIth abdominal tergum and one or two tiny spines near the apex of the inner paraproct lobes.
Emergence is recorded in May and June.

Fig. 9.1. *Leuctra alexanderi* male. VA: Grayson Co., Fox Creek, 25.v.1990, B. Stark, J. Parham, D. Tanner.

Fig. 9.2. *Leuctra ferruginea* female. WI: Lincoln Co., Ripley Creek, 16.viii.1992, C. R. Nelson.

Leuctra ferruginea (Walker)

Adult length 0.3-0.4 inches. Distribution Atlantic Canada to Florida and Mississippi. Males of this species are quite similar to *L. rickeri* but usually the VIIIth tergal lobe is poorly developed.
Emergence occurs from August through December.

Leuctra rickeri James

Adult length 0.3-0.4 inches. Distribution Illinois and West Virginia to Mississippi. Males of this species have a small triangular lobe on the VIIIth abdominal tergum and a distinct spur is present on the inner lobes of the paraprocts.
Emergence is recorded from April through June.

Fig. 9.3. *Leuctra rickeri* female. MS: Simpson Co., Westville Creek tributary, 14.iv.1993, B. Stark.

Fig. 9.4. *Leuctra sibleyi* male. TN: Sevier Co., West Prong Pigeon River, 28.v.1993, B. Stark, R. Simmons, D. Kelly.

Leuctra sibleyi Claassen

Adult length 0.3-0.4 inches. Distribution Atlantic Canada to Illinois and North Carolina. Males of this species have a distinctive, deeply divided lobe on the VIIIth abdominal tergum.

Emergence is recorded from May through June.

Leuctra tenuis (Pictet)

Adult length 0.3-0.4 inches. Distribution Atlantic Canada to Alabama and Oklahoma. Abdominal tergum VII bears a narrow, apically truncate lobe. This structure reaches, at least, the posterior margin of tergum VIII.

Emergence is recorded from late July through September.

Fig. 9.5. *Leuctra tenuis* male. WI: Lincoln Co., Ripley Creek, 16.viii.1992, C. R. Nelson.

Genus *Megaleuctra*

Megaleuctrans, among the rarest of American stoneflies, are most frequently collected around spring seeps of the Appalachians, Pacific Northwest and northern Rocky Mountains. Their unusual size, the presence of six veins in the hindwing anal region and the long ovipositor-like female subgenital plate distinguishes them from other leuctrids. Six species are currently recognized in North America.

Megaleuctra kincaidi Frison

Adult length 0.5-0.7 inches. Distribution Idaho to Oregon and Washington. Males have a pair of acute tubercles on the VIIIth tergum and are distinguished from other *Megaleuctra* species by shape of the structures supporting the epiproct.

Emergence is recorded from April through July.

Fig. 9.6. *Megaleuctra kincaidi* male. OR: Clackamas Co., Still Creek, 5.vi.1991, B. Stark, R. Baumann, C. Henderson.

Fig. 9.7. *Megaleuctra williamsae* female. NC: Jackson Co., Mull Creek, 26.v.1993, B. Stark, R. Simmons, D. Kelly.

Megaleuctra williamsae Hanson

Adult length 0.5-0.7 inches. Distribution Virginia to Tennessee and the Carolinas. Males have a narrow, cylindrical subanal probe curved upward over the abdominal apex.

Emergence is recorded in May and June.

Genus *Moselia*

Moselia currently includes a single species, *M. infuscata*. Adults are unusual leuctrids in having white patches of pigment on the wing margins. Males have a long and hairy, but otherwise unmodified cercal segment and females have a median projection in the subgenital plate notch.

Moselia infuscata (Claassen)

Adult length 0.25-0.4 inches. Distribution mountains of western North America from British Columbia to California and Nevada. This species is often abundant around springs and small streams of the Coast, Cascades and Sierra Nevada Mountains.

Emergence is recorded from March to August.

Fig. 9.8. *Moselia infuscata* female. CA: El Dorado Co., Middle Fork Cosumnes River, 3.v.1995, R. Bottorff.

Genus *Paraleuctra*

Nine species of *Paraleuctra* currently recognized in North America occur primarily in western states and only *P. sara* is known from the East. In the forewings of paraleuctrans, the Rs vein arises beyond the origin of the M vein and in the hind wing the crossveins joining the M and Cu veins is located beyond the point where the Cu vein forks. Males are recognized by the modified and heavily sclerotized cerci and females by the median dorsal sclerotized stripe on segments III-VII.

Paraleuctra occidentalis (Banks)

Adult length 0.3-0.4 inches. Distribution Alaska to California and New Mexico. The male cerci are narrowed apically and excavated on the posterior margin to form a pair of acute processes. In addition the subanal probe is expanded subapically. This species is similar to *P. jewetti* and *P. rickeri*.

Emergence occurs from February through August.

Fig. 9.9. *Paraleuctra occidentalis* female. NM: Santa Fe Co., South Fork Tesuque Creek, 21.v.1991, C. R. Nelson.

Fig. 9.10. *Paraleuctra sara* male. NC: Macon Co., Wayah Creek, 12.iii.1994, B. Stark.

Paraleuctra sara (Claassen)

Adult length 0.3-0.5 inches. Distribution Atlantic Canada to South Carolina. The male cerci have two major horn-like projections.

Emergence is recorded in March and April.

Paraleuctra vershina Gaufin & Ricker

Adult length 0.25-0.35 inches. Distribution western North America from Alaska to California and New Mexico. Males of this common species have bifurcate cerci similar to those of *P. sara*.

Emergence occurs from March through August.

Fig. 9.11. *Paraleuctra vershina* male. CA: El Dorado Co., Sopiago Creek, 3.v.1995, R. Bottorff.

Genus *Perlomyia*

Perlomyia includes two uncommon species, *P. collaris* Banks and *P. utahensis* Needham & Claassen, often associated with spring habitat in the western mountains. Male cerci are sclerotized, and a prominent ventral plate extends from the IXth sternum. No photographs are available for this group.

Genus *Zealeuctra*

Zealeuctra is a group of eight winter, or early spring emerging species, of the Midwest and Southwest. Wing venation is similar to the pattern in *Paraleuctra* but the presence of a cleft IXth male tergum and the absence of a dorsal abdominal stripe readily separate these groups.

Zealeuctra claasseni (Frison)

Adult length 0.25-0.35 inches. Distribution Illinois and Virginia to Texas. Males have a V-shaped cleft on the IXth tergum. Margins of the cleft bear minute serrations.

Emergence is recorded in February and March.

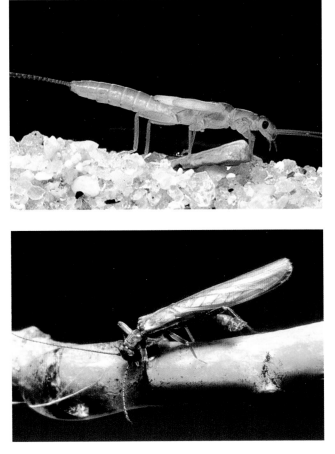

[Clockwise from upper left]

Fig. 9.12. *Zealeuctra claasseni* female. OK: Latimer Co., Rock Creek, 15.ii.1992, B. Stark.

Fig. 9.13. *Zealeuctra hitei* nymph. TX: Travis Co., Little Barton Creek, 14.ii.1992, C. R. Nelson.

Fig. 9.14. *Zealeuctra hitei* male. TX: Travis Co., Little Barton Creek, 12.ii.1992, C. R. Nelson.

Zealeuctra hitei Ricker & Ross

Adult length 0.25-0.35 inches. Distribution Texas. The cleft on the male IXth tergum is similar to that of *Z. claasseni* but lacks lateral serrations. This species is found in intermittent streams of the blackland prairie and Edward's Plateau.

Emergence occurs from November through March.

Zealeuctra warreni Ricker & Ross

Adult length 0.25-0.35 inches.   Distribution Missouri to Arkansas and Oklahoma.   This species occurs with *Z. claasseni* in the Ouachitas but emerges in December and January and has a wider cleft on the IXth tergum.

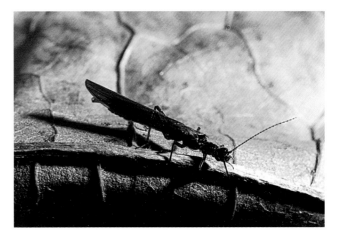

Fig. 9.15. *Zealeuctra warreni* female.   OK: Leflore Co., Big Creek, 16.ii.1992, B. Stark.

CHAPTER 10

FAMILY TAENIOPTERYGIDAE—THE EARLY STONES

The early stones are medium sized and often dark bodied stoneflies with subequal tarsal segments. Nymphs have widely divergent wingpads and those in the five brachypterine genera (*Bolotoperla, Doddsia, Oemopteryx, Strophopteryx, Taenionema*) are without gills but *Taeniopteryx* nymphs have finger-like gills on the coxae. Adults begin emergence during winter in the south and continue through the spring and early summer in the north and at high elevations. The male epiproct is often stout and paraprocts vary from simple plates to complexly lobed structures. Both sexes of brachypterine adults have elongate ventral plates on abdominal segment nine but these structures are absent in *Taeniopteryx*. Fly patterns modeled after these stoneflies are usually called "early browns" or "early blacks". Currently six genera and 35 species are recognized in North America.

Genus *Bolotoperla*

Bolotoperla is represented by a single uncommon Appalachian species, *B. rossi*. Males are atypical of most brachypterines in having a vesicle on sternum IX and the females have a narrow notch and median sclerotized band on sternum VIII. Nymphal specimens have dorsal hair fringes on basal segments of both antennae and cerci.

Bolotoperla rossi (Frison)

Adult length 0.5-0.65 inches. Distribution eastern North America generally along the Appalachians from Quebec to North Carolina. Although collected infrequently, *B. rossi* can be locally abundant in rocky 2nd to 4th order streams. Among eastern brachypterines, this is the only species whose males have both a ventral lobe on segment IX and a pair of slender median projections on tergum X.

Emergence occurs from March through early June.

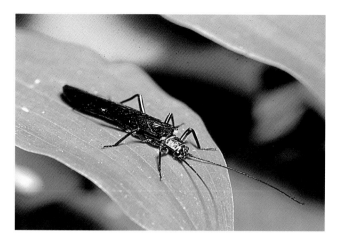

Fig. 10.1. *Bolotoperla rossi* female. VA: Grayson Co., Opossum Creek, 24.v.1994, B. Stark, S. Szczytko, J. Sandberg.

Genus *Doddsia*

Doddsia is represented by a single widely distributed western species, *D. occidentalis*. Adults have distinctively patterned wings and two ocelli. Males bear apically truncate, paired projections on tergum X and the process of the female IXth sternum is shield shaped.

Doddsia occidentalis (Banks)

Adult length 0.4-0.6 inches. Distribution western North America from Alaska to California and New Mexico. The spotted wings and asymmetrical keel on the male IXth sternal plate make this species distinctive among western brachypterines.

Emergence is recorded from February through June.

Fig. 10.2. *Doddsia occidentalis* female. NM: San Miguel Co., Holy Ghost Creek, 23.v.1995, B. Stark, J. Parham.

Genus *Oemopteryx*

Four species of these early browns occur in North America with two eastern and two western forms currently recognized. In two species (*O. fosketti*, *O. glacialis*) the flightless males have curiously shortened and upturned forewings, but in *O. contorta* and *O. vanduzeea* the wings are normal. The only Rocky Mountain species, *O. fosketti*, occurs in large rivers of the Colorado, Saskatchewan and upper Missouri drainage basins.

Oemopteryx glacialis (Newport)

Adult length 0.4-0.6 inches. Distribution eastern North America from Minnesota and Quebec to West Virginia. Males of this species are easily distinguished from *O. contorta*, the other eastern species of this genus, by the shortened forewings and by absence of a vesicle on the IXth sternum.

Emergence occurs from February through March.

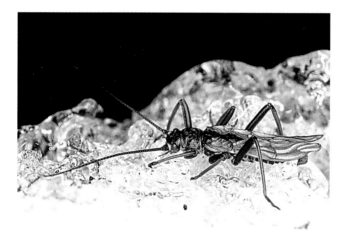

Fig. 10.3. *Oemopteryx glacialis* male. WI: Shawano Co., Wolf River, 18.iii.1992, S. Szczytko, J. Sandberg, J. Cahow.

Fig. 10.4. *Oemopteryx glacialis* nymph. WI: Shawano Co., Wolf River, 18.iii.1992, S. Szczytko, J. Sandberg, J. Cahow.

Oemopteryx vanduzeea (Claassen)

Adult length 0.4-0.6 inches. Distribution Lake Tahoe region of California. This uncommon species has normal length wings and bears a general resemblance to *Taenionema*. Males are distinguished from other western brachypterines by the small vesicle on sternum IX, and in both sexes costal crossveins are absent except for an apical C-R crossvein.

Emergence occurs in April and May.

Fig. 10.5. *Oemopteryx vanduzeea* female. CA: El Dorado Co., intermittent stream, 3.v.1995, R. Bottorff.

Genus *Strophopteryx*

Six species, all from eastern North America, are currently included in this genus but most have distributions restricted to the Ozark-Ouachita or Appalachian Mountain regions. *S. fasciata*, however, is widely distributed in eastern North America. In *Strophopteryx* males, the apex of the IXth sternal process is abruptly upturned and vesicles are absent.

Strophopteryx arkansae Ricker & Ross

Adult length 0.5-0.6 inches. Distribution Ozark and Ouachita Mountains of Arkansas, Missouri and Oklahoma. Males differ from *S. fasciata* in not having the apex of the IXth sternal process sharply upturned.

Emergence occurs in January and early February.

[Clockwise from upper left]

Fig. 10.6. *Strophopteryx arkansae* female. AR: Van Buren Co., Peyton Creek, 4.i.1997, B. Stark, S. Tucker.

Fig. 10.7. *Strophopteryx fasciata* female. WI: Shawano Co., Wolf River, 18.iii.1992, S. Szczytko, J. Sandberg, J. Cahow.

Fig. 10.8. *Strophopteryx fasciata* nymph. WI: Shawano Co., Wolf River, 18.iii.1992, S. Szczytko, J. Sandberg, J. Cahow.

Strophopteryx fasciata (Burmeister)

Adult length 0.4-0.6 inches. Distribution eastern North America from Quebec and Manitoba to Oklahoma, Mississippi and South Carolina. Most males have a pair of conspicuous lobes on tergum IX and the female IXth sternal process is strongly narrowed in the apical half.

Emergence occurs from February through April.

Genus *Taenionema*

Twelve North American *Taenionema* species are currently recognized with one species, *T. atlanticum*, known from the east and the other eleven occuring in the west. *Taenionema* males are similar to those of *Strophopteryx* but the apex of the IXth sternal process is not sharply upturned. These early browns are common throughout the western mountain ranges and from Atlantic Canada along the Appalachians to South Carolina. Stanger & Baumann (1993) reviewed the genus.

Taenionema pacificum (Banks)

Adult length 0.5-0.7 inchex. Distribution western North America from Alaska to California and New Mexico. This species is typically found in large creeks and rivers. Males have moderate sized lobes on tergum X and a distinctively recurved epiproct tip.

Emergence occurs from February through June.

[Clockwise from upper left]

Fig. 10.9. *Taenionema pacificum* male. NM: Lincoln Co., Rio Bonito, 4.iii.1996, B. Stark.

Fig. 10.10. *Taenionema pallidum* female. NM: San Miguel Co., Holy Ghost Creek, 22.v.1995, B. Stark.

Fig. 10.11. *Taenionema pallidum* mating pair. NM: San Miguel Co., Willow Creek, 22.v.1991, S. Szczytko, B. Stark, J. Sandberg.

Taenionema pallidum (Banks)

Adult length 0.4-0.5 inches. Distribution western North America from Yukon to California and New Mexico. This is a common species throughout its range and has an extended emergence from February in the southern Rockies through July. This species, previously known as *T. nigripenne* (or *nigripennis*), is recognized by a truncate apex of the male sternal IX process and by shape of the epiproct.

Taenionema raynorium (Claassen)

Adult length 0.4-0.7 inches. Distribution north central Sierra Nevada Mountains of California. Adults have a large clear band in the apical third of the wings and the lobes of the male 10th tergum are large and truncate.

Emergence occurs from February to June.

Fig. 10.12. *Taenionema raynorium* male. CA: El Dorado Co., Middle Fork Cosumnes River, 3.v.1995, R. Bottorff.

Genus *Taeniopteryx*

Eleven "early black" stonefly species are currently recognized in North America. Two species, *T. nivalis* and *T. parvula* are essentially transcontinental and the others are known from the eastern United States and Canada. *Taeniopteryx* nymphs have finger-like segmented coxal gills and adults retain a distinctive coxal "gill scar". Males have 1-segmented cerci.

Taeniopteryx burksi Ricker & Ross

Adult length 0.4-0.6 inches. Distribution eastern North America from Quebec and Minnesota to Florida and Texas. Males have a vesicle on sternum IX and lack femoral spurs, although some specimens have low swellings on the hind femora.

Emergence occurs from January through March.

Fig. 10.13. *Taeniopteryx burksi* male. AR: Searcy Co., Little Red River, 4.i.1997, B. Stark, S. Tucker.

Taeniopteryx lonicera Ricker & Ross

Adult length 0.35-0.5 inches. Distribution southern United States from Virginia to Florida and Texas. Males have broad, apically rounded paraprocts, modified cerci, and lack a vesicle on sternum IX. This species is most similar to *T. lita*.

Emergence occurs from December through February.

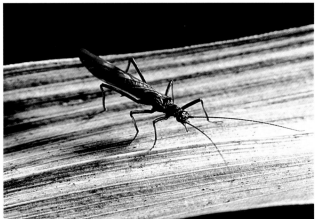

Fig. 10.14. *Taeniopteryx lonicera* female. MS: Simpson Co., Rials Creek, 21.xii.1994, B. Stark.

Fig. 10.15. *Taeniopteryx maura* male. NC: Macon Co., Wayah Creek, 5.i.1993, B. Stark.

Taeniopteryx maura (Pictet)

Adult length 0.4-0.6 inches. Distribution eastern North America from Maine and Minnesota to South Carolina and Texas. Males have a vesicle on sternum IX and distinctive spurs on the hind femora. The paraprocts are slender and apically acute. *T. maura* and *T. burksi* broadly overlap in range and are often difficult to separate, but spur size has often been used as a potential character.

Emergence occurs from January through March.

Taeniopteryx metequi Ricker & Ross

Adult length 0.3-0.4 inches. Distribution Ontario to Kansas, south to Oklahoma, Alabama and North Carolina. Males are long legged, often short winged, and lack a vesicle on sternum IX.

Emergence occurs from December through March.

Fig. 10.16. *Taeniopteryx metequi* male. AR: Searcy Co., Little Red River, 4.i.1997, B. Stark, S. Tucker.

Taeniopteryx nivalis (Fitch)

Adult length 0.5-0.65 inches. Distribution transcontinental from Washington and California to Atlantic Canada. Known as far south as Delaware and Utah. Males are generally similar to *T. maura* but lack spurs on the hind femora.

Emergence occurs from February through April.

Fig. 10.17. *Taeniopteryx nivalis* male. WI: Shawano Co., Wolf River, 18.iii.1992, S. Szczytko, J. Sandberg, J. Cahow.

Fig. 10.18. *Taeniopteryx nivalis* nymph. WI: Shawano Co., Wolf River, 18.iii.1992, S. Szczytko, J. Sandberg, J. Cahow.

CHAPTER 11

FAMILY NEMOURIDAE—THE FORESTFLIES

Nemourids, sometimes called "mottled browns" by fly fishers, are a diverse group of small, spring and summer emerging stoneflies. The distinctive nymphs are brown with divergent hind wingpads and a small 2nd tarsal segment; gills, if present, are usually located in the neck region associated with cervical sclerites. Adults have 1-segmented cerci and the forewings of most genera have an X-pattern of veins at the cord. Forestfly males have a complex, sclerotized epiproct, well developed paraprocts and in most genera a slender vesicle occurs on sternum IX. Presently 65 North American species in 12 genera are known and the world fauna includes more than 400 species.

Genus *Amphinemura*

Sixteen Nearctic species are currently recognized in this large Holarctic group, but five are southwestern forms known from a few sites in Mexico and southern Arizona. Multi-branched cervical gills are present and the filaments arise separately from the gill bases. In eastern North America, this is the only nemourid group with branched cervical gills, but in the west, *Malenka* and one *Zapada* species also share this character.

Amphinemura banksi Baumann & Gaufin

Adult length 0.3-0.4 inches. Distribution Idaho and South Dakota to Colorado and Arizona. Adults of this species and other western *Amphinemura* have "pictured" wings. Species recognition requires careful examination of male epiproct and paraproct structures.

Emergence occurs in July and August.

[Clockwise from upper left]

Fig. 11.1. *Amphinemura banksi* female. CO: Larimer Co., 7.vii.1993, B. Kondratieff.

Fig. 11.2. *Amphinemura delosa* nymph. WI: Waushara Co., Humphrey Creek, 9.v.1991, S. Szczytko, J. Sandberg, J. Cahow.

Fig. 11.3. *Amphinemura delosa* female. WI: Waushara Co., Humphrey Creek, 9.v.1991, S. Szczytko, J. Sandberg, J. Cahow.

Amphinemura delosa (Ricker)

Adult length 0.3-0.4 inches. Distribution Quebec and Michigan to Oklahoma and Georgia. Males of this species have the paraprocts curved over the 10th tergum. Distinctive clusters of spines are located along these structures.

Emergence occurs from March through May.

Amphinemura nigritta (Provancher)

Adult length 0.3-0.4 inches. Distribution Atlantic Canada to Arkansas and Florida. This species is similar to *A. delosa* and can only be distinguished by careful examination of the paraprocts.

Emergence occurs from March through June.

Fig. 11.4. *Amphinemura nigritta* female. MS: Claiborne Co., Ragsdale Creek, 17.iv.1993, B. Stark.

Genus *Lednia*

Lednia includes an uncommon species, *L. tumana* (Ricker) known from Glacier National Park, Montana. Adults and nymphs lack gills and males are the only western nemourids without a vesicle. No photographs are available for this group.

Genus *Malenka*

Malenka is a western Nearctic group closely related to *Amphinemura*. Branched cervical gills occur on nymphs and adults but the branches arise from a stalked base. Males have dorsal lobes on the cerci and females of many species have a nipple-like projection on sternum VII. *Malenka* adults are often found on vegetation around springs where extended emergences are common.

Malenka californica (Claassen)

Adult length 0.35-0.45 inches. Distribution British Columbia and Manitoba to California and Colorado. Males have a sclerotized and sharply pointed cercal lobe and the female subgenital plate notch extends about halfway across sternum VIII.

Emergence occurs from March through December in spring influenced habitat.

Fig. 11.5. *Malenka californica* female. CA: El Dorado Co., Sopiago Creek, 3.v.1995, R. Bottorff.

Fig. 11.6. *Malenka coloradensis* female. NM: Lincoln Co., Rio Bonito, 29.v.1995, B. Stark, C. Massey.

Malenka coloradensis (Banks)

Adult length 0.3-0.4 inches. Distribution South Dakota and Wyoming to Arizona and New Mexico. The male cercal lobes are membranous, rounded structures and the paraprocts are blunt apically but with lateral prongs.

Emergence occurs from June through November.

Malenka depressa (Banks)

Adult length 0.3-0.4 inches. Distribution California and Oregon. The male cercal lobes are large, lightly sclerotized and bluntly rounded and the paraprocts are forked at about mid-length.

Emergence occurs from March through December.

Fig. 11.7. *Malenka depressa* male. CA: El Dorado
Co., Cedar Canyon, 11.v.1995, R. Bottorff.

Genus *Nemoura*

Nemoura is a large, primarily Oriental and Palearctic genus, represented by five species in the Nearctic region. Gills are absent and the male cerci are typically sclerotized and have 1-3 apical spines. The female VIIth sternum forms a tongue-like extension over all or most of sternum VIII.

Nemoura spiniloba Jewett

Adult length 0.3-0.4 inches. Distribution California. This uncommon species was first collected in the Bay area of California but more recently it has been found in the area west of Lake Tahoe. Male cerci are globular, sclerotized, and have a single small apical spine.
Emergence occurs from March through May.

Fig. 11.8. *Nemoura spiniloba* female. CA: El Dorado
Co., intermittent stream, 11.v.1995, R. Bottorff.

Genus *Ostrocerca*

This group includes four species with Appalachian distributions and two known from the Pacific Northwest. Adults and nymphs lack gills and males are recognized by the elongate, curved cerci and by the swollen terminal abdominal segments. No photographs are available for this group.

Genus *Paranemoura*

Paranemoura is represented by two small eastern species, *P. perfecta* and *P. claasseni*. These species lack gills, the cerci are unmodified, and males lack a vesicle. The usual "nemourid X-pattern" of the forewing is also absent in this group.

Paranemoura perfecta (Walker)

Adult length 0.25-0.35 inches. Distribution Atlantic Canada and Ontario to North Carolina. Adults of this small species have banded wings and the apical crossvein usually found between the C and R veins, instead runs between C and Sc, thus interrupting the X-pattern.

Emergence occurs from March through May.

Fig. 11.9. *Paranemoura perfecta* female. NC: Macon Co., Cullasaja River, 14.iii.1995, B. Stark.

Genus *Podmosta*

Podmosta is a group of four western and one northeastern species. They are small, lack gills, the male cerci are unmodified and the male epiproct is a short, thick, complex structure. Females are usually recognized by a median sclerotized band on sternum VIII.

Podmosta delicatula (Claassen)

Adult length 0.25-0.35 inches. Distribution British Columbia and Saskatchewan to California and New Mexico. The male epiproct is broad basally and bears a dorsoapical pair of blunt fork-like processes. The median sclerotized band on the female sternum VIII is narrow and extends across most or all of the segment.

Emergence occurs from April to August.

Fig. 11.10. *Podmosta delicatula* female. CO: Gilpin Co., South Boulder Creek, 28.vi.1995, B. Kondratieff.

Genus *Prostoia*

Prostoia is represented by three eastern Nearctic species (*P. completa, P. hallasi, P. similis*) and a single western species (*P. besametsa*). Nymphs lack gills, the male cerci are unmodified and the adult wings are banded. The male epiproct is long, apically pointed and bears a pair of small basal processes.

Prostoia besametsa (Ricker)

Adult length 0.25-0.4 inches. Distribution Alberta and British Columbia to California and New Mexico. The basal processes of the male epiproct are smaller in this common western species than in other *Prostoia*.
  Emergence occurs from March to August.

Fig. 11.11. *Prostoia besametsa* female. CO: Park Co., North Fork South Platte River, 25.v.1995, B. Stark, M. Mallory, J. Parham.

Genus *Shipsa*

Shipsa includes a single, widely distributed species, *S. rotunda* (Claassen), reported to range from Alabama to Alaska. Adults and nymphs lack gills and males have simple cerci, but the 10th tergum bears a large pair of terminal processes. No photographs are available for this group.

Genus *Soyedina*

Five eastern species and four western species are currently recognized in *Soyedina*. Gills are absent, the wings are rather uniformly brown and in the forewings, veins A1 and A2 join before reaching the wing margin. The male cerci are unmodified, the paraprocts are large and the epiproct typically projects to the rear.

Soyedina carolinensis (Claassen)

Adult length 0.35-0.45 inches. Distribution Delaware and West Virginia to North Carolina and Tennessee. This species is similar to *S. washingtoni* but the two forms are separated on the basis of differences in paraproct shape.
  Emergence occurs from March through April.

Fig. 11.12. *Soyedina carolinensis* female. NC: Macon Co., Blue Valley Overlook, 12.iii.1995, B. Stark, R. Frederick.

Fig. 11.13. *Soyedina nevadensis* female. CA: El Dorado Co., Bendorf Spring, 3.v.1995, R. Bottorff.

Soyedina nevadensis (Claassen)

Adult length 0.35-0.5 inches. Distribution California and Nevada. This species is similar to *S. interrupta* but males of *S. nevadensis* have broad paraproct tips and the mesal margins of these structures are unnotched. *S. interrupta* male paraprocts have narrow tips and their mesal margins are notched.
Emergence occurs from May through July.

Genus *Visoka*

This genus includes an uncommon western species, *V. cataractae* (Neave). Adults and nymphs have branched submental gills, and males have small cerci with delicate apical hooks. No photographs are available for this group.

Genus *Zapada*

This genus is associated primarily with the western mountains where eight species occur but two species (*Z. chila*, *Z. katahdin*) are found in eastern North America. Most species of *Zapada* have four unbranched gills in the neck region but in *Z. cinctipes*, these are 3 or 4-branched. The male cerci are unmodified and the epiproct is often robust.

Zapada cinctipes (Claassen)

Adult length 0.3-0.4 inches. Distribution Alaska and South Dakota to California and New Mexico. This is often the most abundant nemourid species in the Rocky Mountains. It is usually recognized by the branched cervical gills.
Emergence occurs from March through August.

Fig. 11.15. *Zapada frigida* male. CA: El Dorado Co., Tony Gulch, 11.v.1995, R. Bottorff.

Fig. 11.14. *Zapada cinctipes* female and *Capnia* sp. female. CO: Larimer Co., Cache la Poudre River, 14.iii.1991, C. R. Nelson.

Zapada frigida (Claassen)

Adult length 0.3-0.4 inches. Distribution Alaska to California and New Mexico. This is the only *Zapada* species without mottled or banded wings.
Emergence occurs from March through August.

Zapada haysi (Ricker)

Adult length 0.35-0.5 inches. Distribution Alaska to California and New Mexico. The cervical gills are unbranched and without constrictions beyond the base. The male epiproct is membranous dorsally and somewhat ovoid in lateral view.
Emergence occurs from April through July.

Fig. 11.16. *Zapada haysi* female. NM: San Miguel Co., Holy Ghost Creek, 22.v.1995, B. Stark, J. Parham.

BIBLIOGRAPHY

Baumann, R. W. 1975. Revision of the stonefly family Nemouridae (Plecoptera): a study of the world fauna at the generic level. Smithsonian Contributions to Zoology, 211: 1-74.

Baumann, R. W. & D. R. Lauck. 1987. *Salmoperla*, a new stonefly genus from northern California (Plecoptera: Perlodidae). Proceedings of the Entomological Society of Washington, 89: 825-830.

Baumann, R. W., A. R. Gaufin & R. F. Surdick. 1977. The stoneflies (Plecoptera) of the Rocky Mountains. Memoirs of the American Entomological Society, 13: 1-208.

Hitchcock, S. W. 1974. Guide to the insects of Connecticut. Part VII. The Plecoptera or stoneflies of Connecticut. Bulletin of the State Geological and Natural History Survey of Connecticut, 107: 1-262.

Kondratieff, B. C. & R. F. Kirchner. 1993. A reclarification of the males of *Alloperla concolor* and *A. neglecta* (Plecoptera: Chloroperlidae), with new distribution records for both species. Entomological News, 104: 73-78.

Kondratieff, B. C. & R. F. Kirchner. 1991. New Nearctic Chloroperlidae (Plecoptera). Journal of the New York Entomological Society, 99: 199-203.

Kondratieff, B. C., R. F. Kirchner & K. W. Stewart. 1987. A review of *Perlinella* Banks (Plecoptera: Perlidae). Annals of the Entomological Society of America, 89: 24-30.

Leiser, E. & R. H. Boyle. 1982. Stoneflies for the angler. Knopf, New York.

Nelson, C. H. 1984. Numerical cladistic analysis of phylogenetic relationships in Plecoptera. Annals of the Entomological Society of America, 77: 466-473.

Nelson, C. R. & R. W. Baumann. 1989. Systematics and distribution of the winter stonefly genus *Capnia* (Plecoptera: Capniidae) in North America. The Great Basin Naturalist, 49: 289-363.

Nelson, C. R. & R. W. Baumann. 1987. New winter stoneflies of the genus *Capnia* with notes and an annotated checklist of the Capniidae of California (Plecoptera: Capniidae). Entomography, 5: 485-521.

Poulton, B. C. & K. W. Stewart. 1991. The stoneflies of the Ozark and Ouachita Mountains (Plecoptera). Memoirs of the American Entomological Society, 38: 1-116.

Poulton, B. C. & K. W. Stewart. 1988. Aspects of flight behavior in *Calineuria californica* (Plecoptera: Perlidae) from a Rocky Mountain lake outlet system. Entomological News, 99: 125-133.

Richards, C., D. Swisher & F. Arbona, Jr. 1980. Stoneflies. Nick Lyons Books/Winchester Press, New York.

Ricker, W. E. 1952. Systematic studies in Plecoptera. Indiana University Publications, Science Series, 18: 1-200.

Ricker, W. E. & H. H. Ross. 1969. The genus *Zealeuctra* and its position in the family Leuctridae. Canadian Journal of Zoology, 47: 1113-1127.

Ricker, W. E. & H. H. Ross. 1968. North American species of *Taeniopteryx* (Plecoptera, Insecta). Journal of the Fisheries Research Board of Canada, 25: 1423-1439.

Ross, H. H. & W. E. Ricker. 1971. The classification, evolution and dispersal of the winter stonefly genus *Allocapnia*.

Illinois Biological Monographs, University of Illinois Press, 45: 1-166.

Stanford, J. A. & A. R. Gaufin. 1974. Hyporheic communities of two Montana rivers. Science, 185: 700-702.

Stanger, J. A. & R. W. Baumann. 1993. A revision of the stonefly genus *Taenionema* (Plecoptera: Taeniopterygidae). Transactions of the American Entomological Society, 119: 171-229.

Stark, B. P. 1983. A review of the genus *Soliperla* (Plecoptera: Peltoperlidae). The Great Basin Naturalist, 43: 30-44.

Stark, B. P. 1983. The *Tallaperla maria* complex of eastern North America (Plecoptera: Peltoperlidae). Journal of the Kansas Entomological Society, 56: 398-410.

Stark, B. P. 1986. The Nearctic species of *Agnetina* (Plecoptera: Perlidae). Journal of the Kansas Entomological Society, 59: 437-445.

Stark, B. P. 1989. *Perlesta placida* (Hagen), an eastern nearctic species complex (Plecoptera: Perlidae). Entomologica Scandinavica, 20: 263-286.

Stark, B. P. & A. R. Gaufin. 1976. The Nearctic species of *Acroneuria* (Plecoptera: Perlidae). Journal of the Kansas Entomological Society, 49: 221-253.

Stark, B. P. & B. C. Kondratieff. 1987. A new species of *Peltoperla* from eastern North America (Plecoptera: Peltoperlidae). Proceedings of the Entomological Society of Washington, 89: 141-146.

Stark, B. P. & C. R. Nelson. 1994. Systematics, phylogeny and zoogeography of genus *Yoraperla* (Plecoptera: Peltoperlidae). Entomologica Scandinavica, 25: 241-273.

Stark, B. P. & K. W. Stewart. 1982. The nymph of *Viehoperla ada* (Plecoptera: Peltoperlidae). Journal of the Kansas Entomological Society, 55: 494-498.

Stewart, K. W. & P. P. Harper. 1996. Plecoptera, pp. 217-261, *In* R. W. Merritt & K. W. Cummins [eds.], An introduction to the aquatic insects of North America, 3rd ed. Kendall Hunt, Dubuque, Iowa.

Stewart, K. W. & B. P. Stark. 1988. Nymphs of North American stonefly genera (Plecoptera). Thomas Say Foundation, Entomological Society of America, 12: 1-460.

Stewart, K. W., S. W. Szczytko & B. P. Stark. 1983. The language of stoneflies. Bioscience, 33: 117-118.

Surdick, R. F. 1995. New western Nearctic *Sweltsa* (Plecoptera: Chloroperlidae). Proceedings of the Entomological Society of Washington, 97: 161-177.

Surdick, R. F. 1985. Nearctic genera of Chloroperlinae. (Plecoptera: Chloroperlidae). Illinois Biological Monographs, University of Illinois Press, 54: 1-146.

Szczytko, S. W. & K. W. Stewart. 1979. The genus *Isoperla* (Plecoptera) of western North America; holomorphology and systematics, and a new stonefly genus *Cascadoperla*. Memoirs of the American Entomological Society, 32: 1-120.

Index To Common And Scientific Names

125